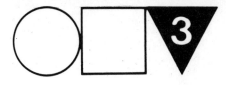

Shape and Size

Nuffield Mathematics Project

John Wiley & Sons Inc., New York

Library of Congress Catalog Card Number: 68-25142

Printed in Great Britain by
Newgate Press Limited
London EC1

General introduction

The aim of the Nuffield Mathematics Project is to devise a 'contemporary approach for children from 5 to 13'. The guides do not comprise an entirely new syllabus. The stress is on *how to learn*, not on what to teach. Running through all the work is the central notion that the children must be set free to make their own discoveries and think for themselves, and so achieve understanding, instead of learning off mysterious drills. In this way the whole attitude to the subject can be changed and 'Ugh, no, 1 didn't like maths' will be heard no more.

To achieve understanding young children cannot go straight to abstractions—they need to handle things ('apparatus' is too grand a word for at least some of the equipment concerned—conkers, beads, scales, globes, and so on).

But 'setting the children free' does not mean starting a riot with a roomful of junk for ammunition. The changeover to the new approach brings its own problems. The guide *I do, and I understand* (which is of a different character from the others) faces these problems and attempts to show how they can be overcome.

The other books fall into three categories: Teachers' Guides, Weaving Guides and Check-up Guides. The Teachers' Guides cover three main topics: ● Computation and Structure, ▼ Shape and Size, ■ Graphs Leading to Algebra. In the course of these guides the development of mathematics is seen as a spiral. The same concept is met over and over again and illustrated in a different way at every stage. The books do not cover years, or indeed any specific time; they simply develop themes and therefore show the teacher how to allow one child to progress at a different pace to another. They contain direct teaching suggestions, examples of apparently un-mathematical subjects and situations which can be used to develop a mathematical sense,

examples of children's work, and suggestions for class discussions and out-of-school activities. The Weaving Guides are single-concept books which give detailed instructions or information about a particular subject.

The third category of books, as the name implies, will provide 'check-ups' on the children's progress. The traditional tests are difficult to administer in the new atmosphere of individual discovery and so our intention is to replace these by individual check-ups for individual children. These are being prepared by a team from the Institut des Sciences de l'Education in Geneva under the general supervision of Piaget. These check-ups, together with more general commentary, will be issued in the same format as the other guides and, in fact, be an integral part of the scheme.

While the books are a vital part of the Nuffield Mathematics Project, they should not be looked on as guides to the only 'right' way to teach mathematics. We feel very strongly that development from the work in the guides is more important than the guides themselves. They were written against the background of teachers' centres where ideas put forward in the books could be discussed, elaborated and modified. We hope very much that they will continue to be used in this way. A teacher by himself may find it difficult to use them without the reassurance and encouragement which come from discussion with others. Centres for discussion do already exist and we hope that many more will be set up.

The children's work that has been reproduced in these books, like the books themselves, is not supposed to be taken as a model of perfection. Some of it indeed contains errors. It should be looked upon as an example of work that children *might* produce rather than a model of work that they *should* produce.

Foreword

The last few years have been exciting ones for teachers of mathematics ; and for those of us who are amateurs in the subject but have a taste for it which was not wholly dulled by the old methods that are so often stigmatised, there has been abundant interest in seeing the new mathematical approach develop into one of the finest elements in the movement towards new curricula.

This is a crucial subject ; and, since a child's first years of work at it may powerfully affect his attitude to more advanced mathematics, the age range 5 to 13 is one which needs special attention. The Trustees of the Nuffield Foundation were glad in 1964 to build on the forward-looking ideas of many people and to set up the Nuffield Mathematics Project ; they were also fortunate to secure Dr. Geoffrey Matthews and other talented and imaginative teachers for the development team. The ideas of this team have helped in the growth of much lively activity, throughout the country, in new mathematical teaching for children : the Schools Council, the Local Education Authority pilot areas, and many individual teachers and administrators have made a vital contribution to this work, and the Trustees are very grateful for so much readiness to co-operate with the Foundation. The fruits of co-operation are in the books that follow ; and many a teacher will enter the classroom with a lively enthusiasm for trying out what is proposed in these pages.

Brian Young
Director of the Nuffield Foundation

Contents

Introduction   1

1   Rigid or non-rigid 2D frameworks   2

2   More about parallels and angles   9

3   Patterns on circles   11

4   Another look at symmetry   23

5   Tile patterns – tessellations   27

6   Angles and turning   29

7   More about polygons and tessellations   32

8   Tables   43

9   Another look at rotational symmetry   48

10   Polyhedra   55

11   Back to transformations   60

Appendix   64

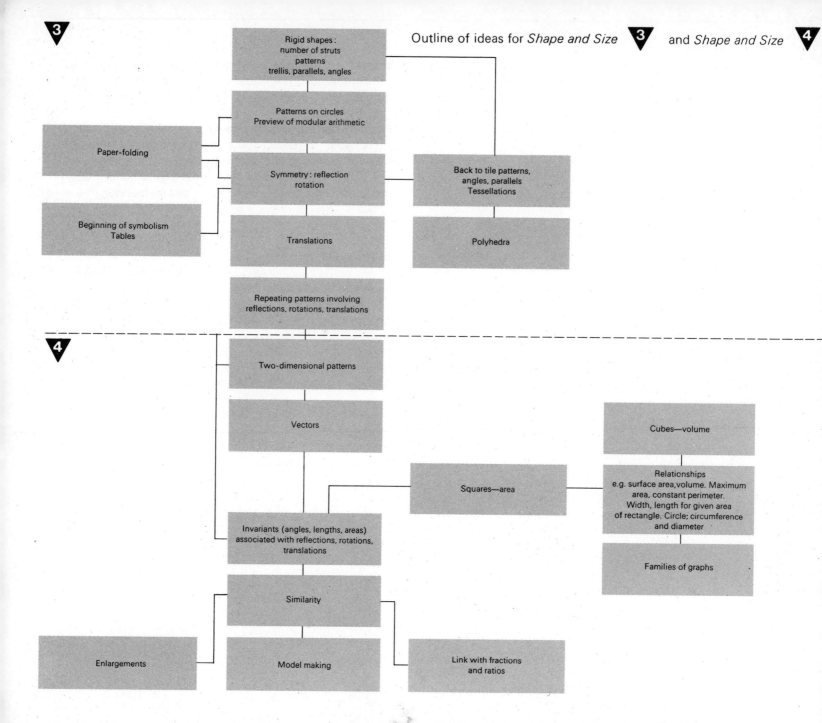

3 ▼

Rigid shapes:
number of struts
patterns
trellis, parallels, angles

Outline of ideas for *Shape and Size* **3** ▼ and *Shape and Size* **4** ▼

Patterns on circles
Preview of modular arithmetic

Paper-folding

Symmetry: reflection
rotation

Back to tile patterns,
angles, parallels
Tessellations

Beginning of symbolism
Tables

Translations

Polyhedra

Repeating patterns involving
reflections, rotations, translations

4 ▼

Two-dimensional patterns

Vectors

Cubes—volume

Squares—area

Relationships
e.g. surface area, volume. Maximum
area, constant perimeter.
Width, length for given area
of rectangle. Circle; circumference
and diameter

Invariants (angles, lengths, areas)
associated with reflections, rotations,
translations

Families of graphs

Similarity

Enlargements

Model making

Link with fractions
and ratios

Introduction

This guide follows on from *Shape and Size* ▼², but before suggesting ideas which might be tried out in the classroom, it might be worth while looking back at the plan and some of the ideas in ▼ and also at the plan for further development.

It will be remembered that ▼² was in three sections. Section I was an introduction which attempted to give a general picture of the aims of, and the approach to, the series; how these could be linked with the rest of the mathematics, the rest of the class activity and the rest of the children's lives; and some of the mathematical principles involved. Section II was a conspectus of ideas for the whole ▼ series covering the primary-school age range, and Section III indicated how some of these ideas could be developed in the classroom with young children in the first years of the junior school. At the end of Section II there was a diagram which showed how the activities suggested in Section III would be continued in ▼³ to cover the older age groups in the junior school. From a further consideration of this diagram it has now been decided to cover the ideas involved in two guides, ▼³ and ▼⁴, instead of one. An outline plan for this is given in the diagram opposite.

It is not intended to repeat here all the ideas discussed in Sections I and II of ▼². Teachers should refer back to these to get a general picture of *Shape and Size* and also to see where particular topics in ▼³ and ▼⁴ fit into the overall plan for the whole series. In fact those sections serve as an introduction to the whole ▼ series for the primary school. The present guide, then, will consist largely of suggestions for children's activities which follow on from those given in Section III of ▼², and in turn will be followed by more activities in ▼⁴.

The activities in ▼² were under four headings:

1. Filling three-dimensional space

The idea of a three-dimensional object or shape occupying a space; the amount of space in a container; conservation of volume; and activities leading to measurement and comparison of volume and capacity. Preliminary discussion of the need for a standard unit. (No mention of calculating volume of cuboids, etc. by using linear dimensions.) How cubes and cuboids fit together. The 'square corner' and first notions of a right angle. Horizontal and vertical.

2. From three dimensions to two

Fitting shapes together (tiles, etc.) Symmetry through observation, patterns, folding, and so on, and the idea of an axis of symmetry. Covering a surface for first notions of area, leading to the square as a suitable unit, but no mention of the generalised way of calculating the areas of rectangular shapes.

3. More about angles

Right angles and half right angles. First stages in drawing plans. Perpendicular and parallel (and for the teacher another look at equivalence relations, cf. *Mathematics Begins* ❶ and *Computation and Structure* ❷).

4. Classification of 2D shapes

Developed from sorting activities similar to those in *Mathematics Begins* ❶ , leading on to a look at properties of some quadrilaterals and how this can be associated with the beginnings of logical argument, and to methods of sorting numbers.

The above summary is a reminder of some of the activities in ▼² which can now be amplified in ▼³ and ▼⁴. Opposite is a diagram which outlines the ideas for inclusion in these further guides. Reference to the Conspectus of Ideas in ▼² will enable teachers to see how these form part of the continuous development of *Shape and Size*.

1 Rigid or non-rigid 2D frameworks

Just as in the early activities in ▼ when we looked for material which would serve as an overlap with *Beginnings* ▼ (in that case filling containers with sand and water) so here we can use some of the material from the later activities in ▼ as a starting-point. In looking at the properties and classification of 2D shapes, children used punched strips of card, plastic, or metal to make frames of these shapes. These punched strips can now be used for further activities.

When the children were doing this work they discovered that some of the shapes could be moved to make other shapes. For instance, one of the activities was to make a rectangle frame by moving strips forming a parallelogram; and in another the children found that a rhombus and a square could be made by moving the same strips into different positions. They can now try to discover if there is something they can do to prevent these frames moving to make different shapes: whether there is a way of making a 2D frame rigid.

As before, children should work in small groups. A group will require at least 12 punched strips (cardboard, plastic, or metal) similar to those used in activities in the section on classification of 2D shapes (▼), and some push-through paper fasteners.

Teachers should recall the word 'polygon' used in *Shape and Size* ▼ for any 2D plane shape bounded by any number of straight edges. Shapes of polygons were made as frames with the punched strips, and a similar procedure is to be used now.

Use the punched strips and paper fasteners to make a shape with three edges.
Take some more strips and make a shape with four edges, and another with five edges.
See if you can move any of the shapes to make different shapes. Is there any shape which cannot be moved out of shape in this way?
Undo the strips and make some more shapes with three sides, four sides, six sides, and so on. Test each shape to see if it can be distorted. You may have to undo the strips to make other shapes so remember to test each as soon as you have made it.
What name can you give to the shapes which cannot be moved, which remain rigid?

Discuss with the children the names of shapes made as frames with four sides, five sides, six sides, and so on. See if they can remember these from previous experiences (▼). Introduce the idea of **regular** polygons, for which the sides are all of equal length and the angles between neighbouring pairs are the same.

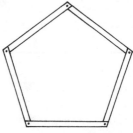

Square : regular

Regular pentagon

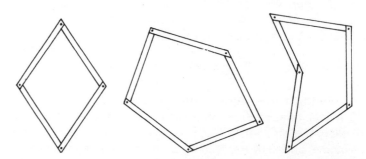

A rhombus : not regular as the angles are not all equal

Pentagons which are not regular although the sides are all equal

Card 6

number of sides in frame	number of struts to make the frame rigid	number of triangles formed when the frame is rigid
3	0	1
4	1	2
5	2	3
6	3	4
7	4	5
8	5	6

My Graph shows the number of triangles formed when a certain frame is made rigid.

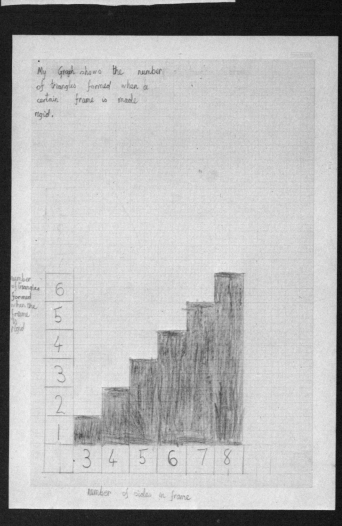

number of triangles formed when the frame is rigid

6
5
4
3
2
1

3 4 5 6 7 8

number of sides in frame

Card 7

The number of triangles formed is one more each time than the number of struts used to make the shapes rigid.

number of sides in frame	number of struts to make the frame rigid	number of triangles made when the frame is made rigid
9	6	7
10	7	8
11	8	9
12	9	10
20	17	18
24	21	22
100	97	98

Card 8

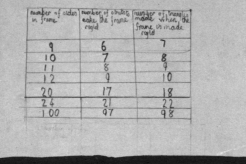

The shapes are made rigid by placing struts to stop it moving.

This is necessary to stop the roof coming down and struts strengthen it

motorway-bridge showing triangles as supports.

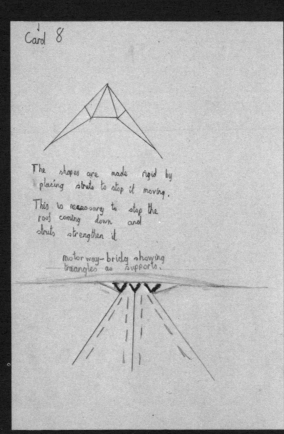

My Graph shows the
number of struts
used to make
shapes with a
certain number
of sides rigid

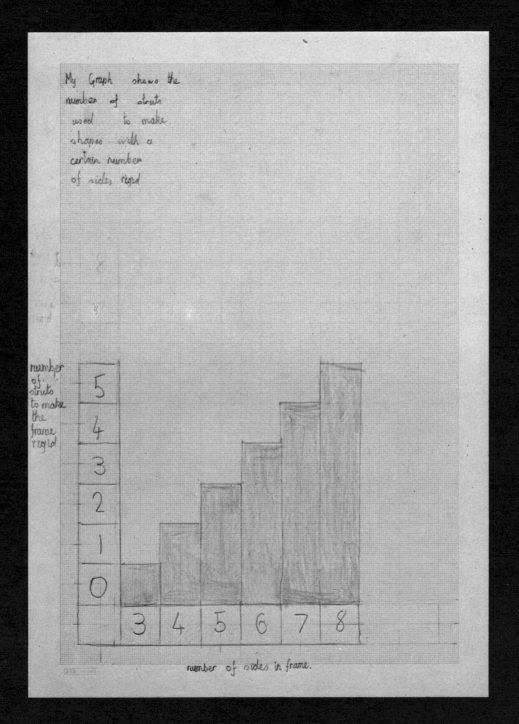

number of sides in frame.

The next step is to see if polygons made as frames can be made rigid by using additional strips.

> Make a four-sided shape using punched strips and paper fasteners. See if you can make this shape rigid, so that it will not move, by adding another strip as a strut. What shapes do you notice inside the frame when you have made it rigid?

> Make some more frames, with five sides, six sides, seven sides, eight sides. Try to make them rigid by fastening additional strips as struts.

This provides an opportunity for discussion about the most economical way of using additional strips as struts to make the frames rigid. Children should be allowed to experiment in their own way first. Results may vary; for instance, with a pentagon the following have been observed:

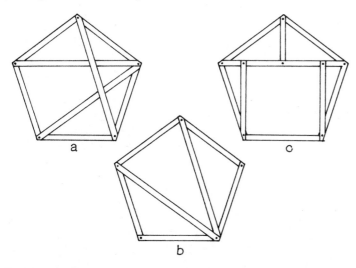

a
c
b

Find which children have used the least number of struts in a case like this. If they have not already done so, suggest that they start at one 'corner' and from this join struts to others as shown at (b). Continue in a similar fashion with frames with six sides, seven sides, eight sides, etc. Preserve these rigid frames for future use.

Ask what shapes they can now see inside the frame when struts have been added in this way to make it rigid (triangles).

> See if you can answer these questions from what you have done.
> Which shape was rigid without adding any more struts?
> What shapes did you see inside the frames when you made them rigid by adding struts?

> Look at the frames you have made rigid.
> Make a table like this: use your discoveries to complete the table.

number of sides in the frame	number of struts needed to make the frame rigid	number of triangles formed when the frame is rigid
3	0	1
4		
5		
6		
7		
8		

Try to find patterns from your table.
Can you see the pattern of numbers for the number of sides and the number of struts? If so, continue your table to at least twelve sides.
Can you see the pattern of numbers for the number of sides and the number of triangles? If so, continue your table to at least twelve sides.
See if you can answer these:
How many struts must be added to make frames with the following number of sides rigid: twenty, twenty-four, one hundred?
How many triangles are formed in each of these?

> Look about the school to find where triangles are used in this way to make a shape rigid, or to stop it from moving out of shape. Make drawings of some of these and write about how the shapes are made rigid, and explain, if you can, why this is necessary.
> Try to find more examples outside the school, on the way home, in the street, in buildings, in bridges, and so on.

This could even be used as a starting-point for a topic' on buildings and bridges. It affords a useful link with history, architecture, local geography, science, and so on, for in addition to finding the use of triangles in bridge girders, etc., some children will no doubt discover the use of the arch, and other shapes. Simple experiments to show the strength of arches, cylindrical girders, girders with square or rectangular cross section, and so on, as well as those made as frames with triangles, are suggested in many books on junior science. The development of the bridge, and the use of the arch in architecture, can be associated with history studies.

The main points arising from the previous activities
Discovery of the triangle as the shape for a rigid frame, and application of this to the conditions of rigidity for other polygonal frames.
Vocabulary: recapitulation of names of polygons (regular and irregular) and diagonal.
Application of discoveries to everyday things.
Discovery of number patterns arising from rigidity of polygons, leading perhaps with some children to a generalised way of expressing this, e.g. for any number of sides n, number of struts is $(n - 3)$, number of triangles is $(n - 2)$.

2 More about parallels and angles

In *Shape and Size* ▼ children were introduced to the idea of **parallel**, and they investigated properties of some 2D shapes which had parallel sides. Teachers should recall these ideas. We can now use some of the material such as punched strips of card, metal, or plastic, from the previous assignments, to find out more about parallels and angles. A piece of trellis used for garden fencing is useful for this, or punched strips can be fastened with paper fasteners to give the action of trellis work.

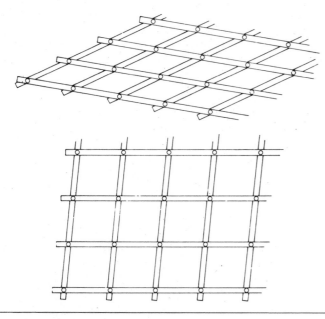

For the next activity the simplified protractor can be used as a 'carrier' in the manner described in *Shape and Size* ▼, pp. 13, 78.

> Open out your trellis work again.
> Try to find angles which look the same size.
> Check them with a piece of folded paper, or by using the protractor. Try this with the trellis work in several different positions.

The angles to look for are:

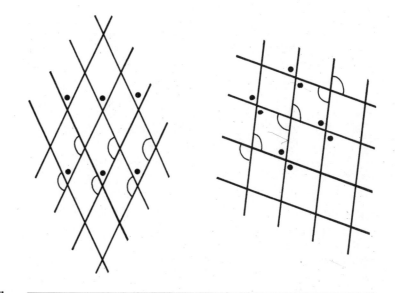

> Start with your trellis work closed up.
> Now open it out a little way.
> What do you notice about the struts which make up the trellis? Do they look parallel?
> Now open the trellis out more. Are the struts still parallel?
> Try it in different positions. Can you see anything that does change?
> Look at the lengths between the joints. Do these distances change when you open and close the trellis work?
> Write about the things which appear to be unchanged and those that change when you move the trellis work.

> Look at the different shapes you can make with your trellis work.
> Try to make some with right angles in them.
> What are the names of the shapes you can make inside the trellis work?

The results depend upon the lengths between the joints of the struts. Some children may produce parallelograms which can be moved to give rectangles; others may produce rhombuses which can be moved to give squares. (Such work was done with punched strips in the last chapter on classification of 2D shapes in *Shape and Size* ▼, and can be recalled now.)

Move the trellis work so that you have right angles where the
struts cross. Check these with a folded-paper right angle.
How many right angles are formed at each crossing-point?
Open the trellis work so that there are no right angles.
Can you see any angles which fit together in pairs to make two
right angles?
Draw a picture to show this and mark such angles in colour.

Parallel lines and angles can be further investigated by placing
a ruler across the lines in an exercise book, or a long piece of
wood with a straight edge across shelves, thus:

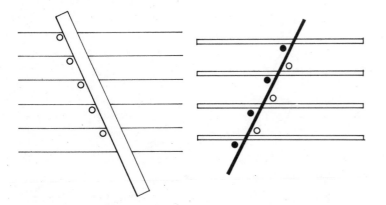

Children can discover angles which look the same size and
check with folded paper or simplified protractor. **No measurement in degrees should be attempted at this stage,** the main
consideration being observation of shapes and angles formed
by trellis work, and angles formed by a transversal meeting a
set of parallel lines. We shall discuss a further development
of this later, as a 'test' for parallel lines. The shapes formed
by the trellis work will also be considered further when we
return to tile patterns and tessellations.

3 Patterns on circles

At this stage in *Computation and Structure* ❷ children will be meeting the first idea of modular arithmetic through 'clocks' and remainders. Here is an extract (p. 86) :

We can see from using the 12-hour clock that we are concerned only with numbers from 1 to 12. Unlike the continentals we stop at 12 and go back to 1, 2, 3, etc. If we can persuade children to accept that '12' on the clock could be re-christened zero (as a starting-point) we can introduce remainder or 'modular' arithmetic and construct tables and patterns from this.

mod 12

+	0	1	2	3	4	5	6	7	8	9	10	11
0	0	1	2	3	4	5	6	7	8	9	10	11
1	1	2	3	4	5	6	7	8	9	10	11	0
2	2	3	4	5	6	7	8	9	10	11	0	1
3	3	4	5	6	7	8	9	10	11	0	1	2
4	4	5	6	7	8	9	10	11	0	1	2	3
5	5	6	7	8	9	10	11	0	1	2	3	4
6	6	7	8	9	10	11	0	1	②	3	4	5
7	7	8	9	10	11	0	1	2	3	4	5	6
8	8	9	10	11	0	1	2	3	4	5	6	7
9	9	10	11	0	1	2	3	4	5	6	7	8
10	10	11	0	1	2	3	4	5	6	7	8	9
11	11	0	1	2	3	4	5	6	7	8	9	10

We have replaced '12' on the clock by '0', and we now have the addition table 'modulo 12'. We start at 0 and when we pass 11 we count on 0, 1, 2, 3, . . . instead of 12, 13, 14, 15, . . . , so that 13 is replaced by 1, 14 by 2, etc. just as on the clock. As an example, the arrows indicate 6 and 8 and where the '6' row and '8' column intersect shows 2. This means that the result of adding the numbers 6 and 8 'modulo 12' is 2. A model for this is, of course, to set a clock at 6 o'clock and move it on by 8 hours. It will then read 2.

Of course it is possible to consider arithmetic modulo other numbers, e.g., a five-hour clock would lead to arithmetic 'mod 5'.

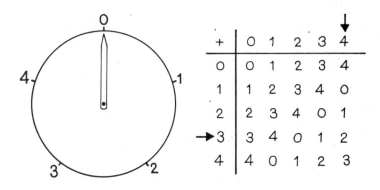

+	0	1	2	3	4
0	0	1	2	3	4
1	1	2	3	4	0
2	2	3	4	0	1
3	3	4	0	1	2
4	4	0	1	2	3

e.g. $3 + 4 = 2$ (mod 5). On the clock, counting round from zero to 3, and then a further 4, leads to the '2' mark.

Modular arithmetic is useful in that when dealing with a finite set of integers we can frequently get a clearer picture of some of the underlying structure and the operational rules of mathematics. These occur in geometrical situations as well as in number, and modular arithmetic affords one way of linking these. A fuller consideration of this is given in *Computation and Structure* ❹ and also later in this guide.

We are mainly concerned here with the idea of thinking about remainders, and to assist this, patterns and shapes produced by stitching or drawing on circles can be used. This can be based on the twelve divisions of a clock-face. Although a group of children might be engaged in this activity it is essentially an individual one and each child can produce his own shapes and patterns. Several circular shapes will be required by each child. For drawing patterns, plain paper is adequate, but for stitching, thin card or manilla will be necessary. Circles can be drawn on sheets of paper or thin card either by using a circular-shaped object (such as a tin lid); or by using compasses, in which case this provides an opportunity for introduction of these instruments.

As the patterns are based on the twelve divisions of a clock-face, some thought must be given to the marking of these. A useful radius for the circle for this work is about two inches. Clock-face markers can be obtained which have the twelve hour-marks indicated by holes. These may be used to mark the circles for patterns, but as these markers are usually of about one-inch radius, some other method may be required. Paper-folding is one way. A circle of radius about two inches should be drawn on cartridge paper and cut out, or a filter paper of about this size may be used. (Filter papers can also be used for some of the pattern work.) The paper is folded as shown in the diagram:

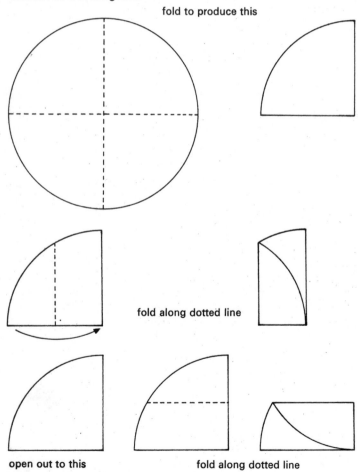

fold to produce this

fold along dotted line

open out to this

fold along dotted line

On opening out the paper, the creases will appear as below:

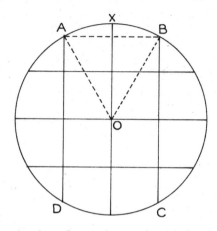

This divides the circumference into twelve equal parts, and can be used as a template for marking other circles.

For the teacher's information
In the rectangle ABCD folding shows that AB is half the diameter of the circle, so in triangle ABO we have AB = BO = AO (all equal to a radius).

ABO is equilateral, and so the measure of each angle is 60 degrees.

Again from the folding we see that angle BOX is half angle BOA so angle BOX = 30 degrees.

This is $\frac{1}{12}$ of 360 degrees, and so XB is $\frac{1}{12}$ of the circumference.

The same idea can be carried out for the other points on the circumference, and we see that this method of folding divides the circumference into twelve equal parts.

The use of compasses and the folding of paper will have been guided by the teacher. Once a template of a 'clock' with twelve divisions has been made it can be used to mark circles for pattern work. The following suggestions are for the children, and start from the ready-made circles (one is shown here). The patterns may be drawn in coloured pencil.

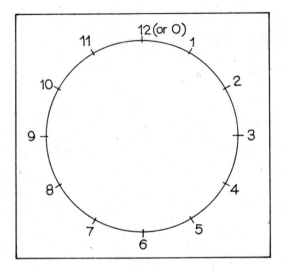

As an alternative a circle nail-board and coloured rubber bands can be used. These boards can be bought from educational suppliers or made from five-ply wood with three-quarter-inch panel pins driven in at the appropriate places. A cardboard template can be used to mark the twelve points. Boards such as this have the advantage that errors due to drawing do not arise.

> Start at 1. Join 1 to 2; 2 to 3; 3 to 4, and so on.
> When you reach 12, join to 1 to complete your pattern.
> Try to find the name of the shape you have made.

Similar 'assignments' can be given starting at one and adding on two each time (1 to 3, 3 to 5, etc.) The sequence should be noticed: 1, 3, 5, 7, 9, 11, 1, and discussed, noting that when $11+2=13$, 13 is replaced by 1.

Adding 3 gives 1, 4, 7, 10, 1.

Adding 4 gives 1, 5, 9, 1.

In some of the following patterns it may help if small arrow marks → are put on the lines to show in which way the joins are made.

> Start at 1. Add 5 each time. Join 1 to 6, 6 to 11. Now add 5 to 11. Which point do you reach?
> Carry on in this way until you arrive back at 1.
> What would you call the shape you have made?
> Write the order in which you joined the points, beginning like this: 1, 6, 11, ... and ending with 1.

Teachers should discuss this sequence:
1, 6, 11, 4, 9, 2, 7, 12, 5, 10, 3, 8, 1
and such joins as $11 + 5 = 16$, but as we start again at 12, 16 becomes 4, and so on.

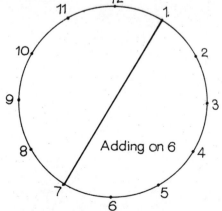

Adding on 6

Do more patterns and discuss the sequence of joining-points, and the shapes produced, e.g.

Start at 1
Add 6 (1, 7, 1).
Add 7 (1, 8, 3, 10, 5, 12, 7, 2, 9, 4, 11, 6, 1).
Compare this with the pattern and sequence from 'adding 5'.
Add 8 (1, 9, 5, 1) compare with 'Adding 4'.
Add 9 (1, 10, 7, 4, 1) compare with 'Adding 3'.
Add 10 (1, 11, 9, 7, 5, 3, 1) compare with 'Adding 2'.
Add 11 (1, 12, 11, 10, 9, 8, 7, 6, 5, 4, 3, 2, 1).
Compare with 'Adding 1'.

Children should be encouraged to describe how the patterns and shapes were made, and this and the sequence of numbers can be written alongside or under each. The patterns can make an attractive display.

The above suggestions provide experiences leading to later work on modular arithmetic and remainders. In this case this is not strictly modulo 12, as the 'remainder' when any point is joined to 12 should be 0. But it offers an enjoyable way of introducing some of the ideas.

Patterns on other 'clocks' can be attempted. It is easy to mark the circumference with six equal parts using the folded-paper marker. Children can then join points in a similar way to that for the twelve-point circle.

Teachers can give 'assignments' as previously suggested. Starting at 1 each time the following will arise:
Adding 1. 1, 2, 3, 4, 5, 6, 1.
Adding 2. 1, 3, 5, 1.
Adding 3. 1, 4, 1.
Adding 4. 1, 5, 3, 1.
Adding 5. 1, 6, 5, 4, 3, 2, 1.

Nail-boards can be obtained with twenty-four equal divisions on the circumference of the circle, and more able children may like to experiment with patterns on these.

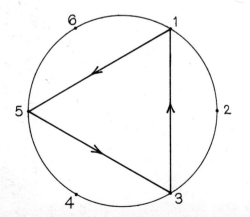

The following four illustrations show clock patterns stitched on to thin cardboard. The heavy lines show the threads visible on the front of the card, the lighter ones those showing through from the back.

12 Clock.

5 or 7 at a time.

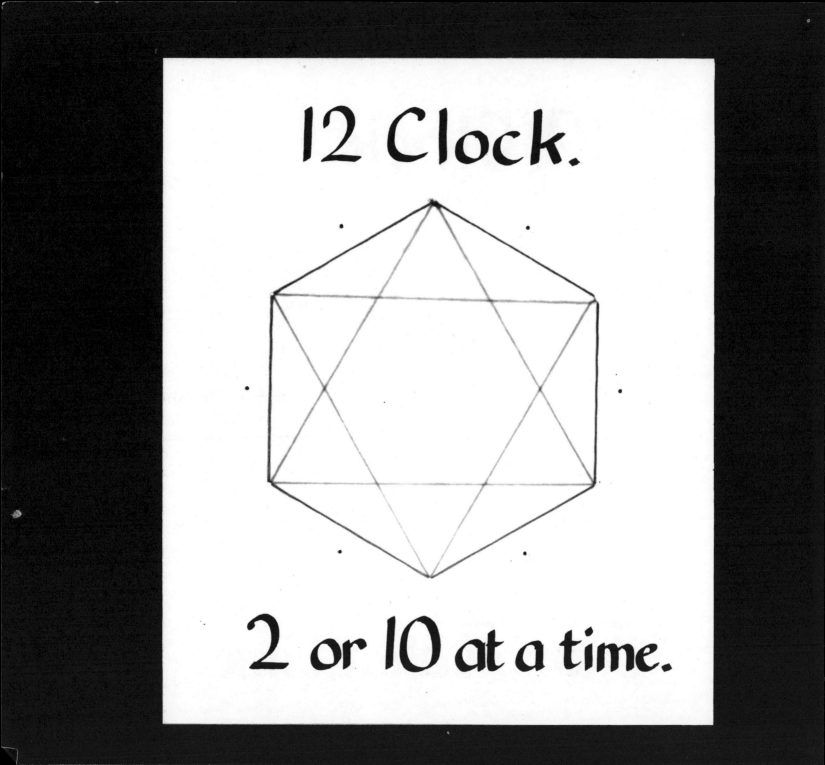

9 Clock.

1 or 8 at a time.

II Clock.

5 or b at a time.

Reflectional Symmetry in Patterns.

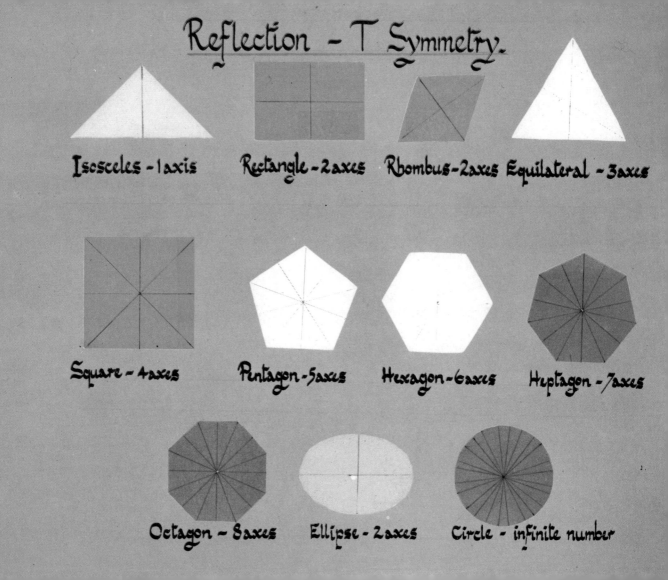

Reflection - T Symmetry.

Isosceles - 1 axis   Rectangle - 2 axes   Rhombus - 2 axes   Equilateral - 3 axes

Square - 4 axes   Pentagon - 5 axes   Hexagon - 6 axes   Heptagon - 7 axes

Octagon - 8 axes   Ellipse - 2 axes   Circle - infinite number

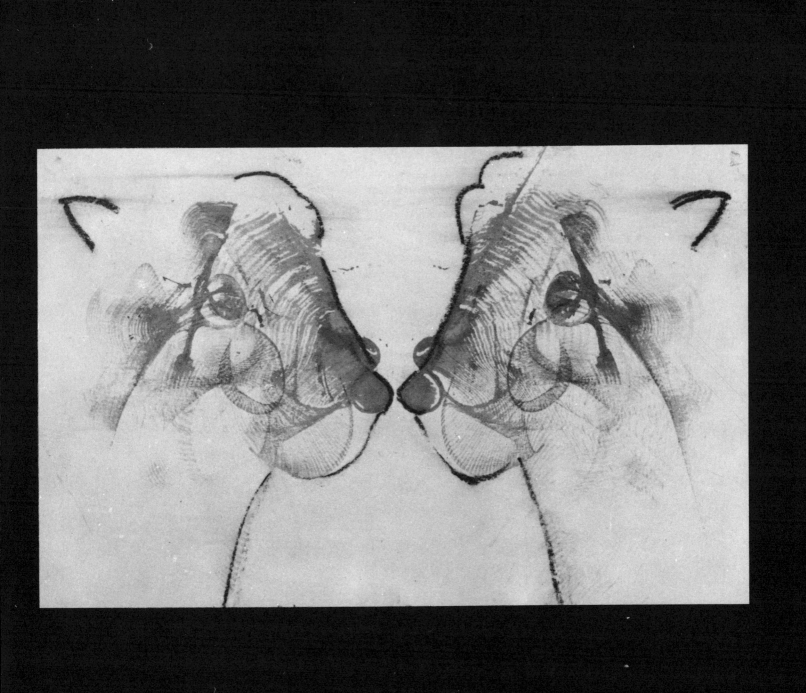

Rotational Symmetry.

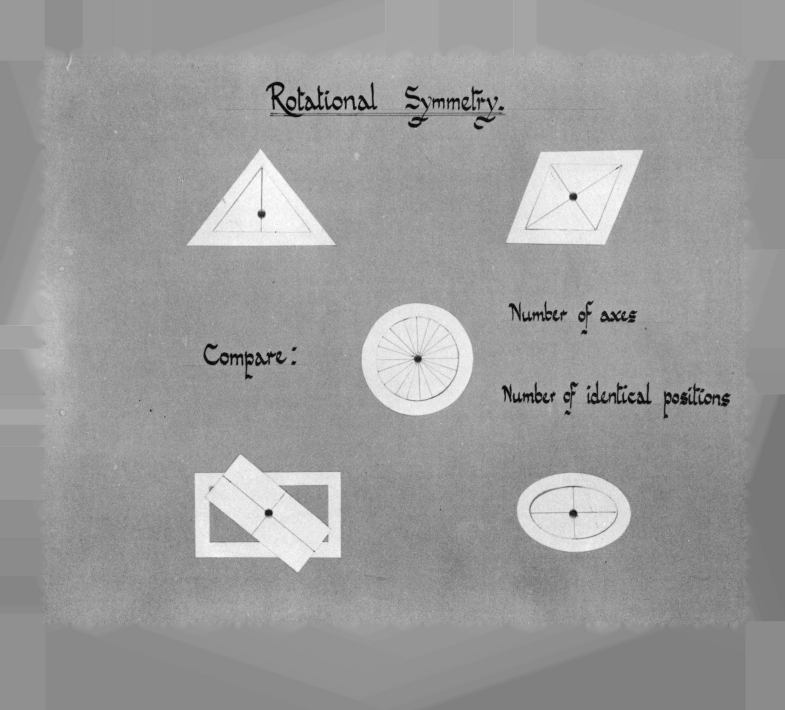

Compare:

Number of axes

Number of identical positions

4 Another look at symmetry

Symmetry was investigated in mainly through observation and pattern work. In 3D this was one of the notions brought out in discovering the ways in which a cuboid, such as a brick, could be replaced. This led on to a similar approach in 2D through replacing tiles, and then to the idea of 'balance' about an axis of symmetry in patterns and paper-folding. The investigation introduced the ideas of reflection and rotation, which were also outlined in the introduction to .

We can now take another look at symmetry and develop some of the ideas first experienced in *Shape and Size* . In their discoveries children found that a rectangular piece of paper, for instance, could be folded along an axis of symmetry:

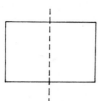

and that, in fact, it had two axes of symmetry:

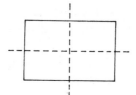

This was an example of **reflection**. They also discovered in their work with rectangular tiles that the tile could be turned through two right angles about a point at its centre and would fit into the hole.

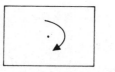

This was an example of **rotational symmetry**.

We shall keep to this notation at present although some books refer to the dotted lines as 'lines' rather than 'axes' of symmetry.

In the following suggestions teachers should be aware that most standard type faces destroy the symmetry of capital letters in order to increase legibility. For these activities a 'symmetricised' alphabet is required.

Here is an alphabet printed in capital letters :

A B C D E F G H I J K L M N O P Q R S T U V W X Y Z

Look at A. It is 'balanced' about the dotted line, the axis of symmetry.
Write down all the other letters which appear balanced about an 'up and down' axis of symmetry like A. Show the axis by a dotted line.

A B C D E F G H I J K L M N O P Q R S T U V W X Y Z

Look at K. It is balanced about the dotted line, the axis of symmetry.

Write down all the other letters which appear balanced about an 'across the page' axis of symmetry like K. Show the axis by a dotted line.

A B C D E F G H I J K L M N O P Q R S T U V W X Y Z

N. This letter looks the same if you turn it through half a complete turn about the point marked.

Find all the other letters which look the same when turned in this way.

The children can then make lists to show the sets of letters which

a have an 'up and down' axis of symmetry
b have an 'across the page' axis of symmetry
c are included in both sets — have two axes of symmetry
d have rotational symmetry — can be turned through half a complete turn about a point.

Various ways of illustrating classification have been suggested in *Mathematics Begins* ❶ and *Shape and Size* ❷ . These could be used for the sets of letters given on p. 23.

Some of the 2D shapes encountered in the activities in ❷ can also be investigated in a similar way. Coloured gummed paper can be used, and the shapes traced round card templates. These can be cut out and folded to find axes of symmetry (lines). Rotational symmetry can also be investigated. Suitable shapes for these activities are: squares, rectangles, parallelograms, rhombuses, equilateral triangles, isosceles triangles, regular hexagons, and so on — including circles.

An assignment might be:

> Cut out a square from coloured paper. Fold it so that each half fits exactly on the other half. In how many ways can you fold the square so that this happens?
> How many axes of symmetry has a square?

The other shapes can be treated in a similar manner and display mounted, with a description of the activity.

Children should be encouraged to look for examples in natural and man-made objects, in pictures, advertisements, etc., which exhibit symmetry in this way; and to make a display indicating the axes of symmetry.

It might be worth pointing out that much so-called 'symmetry' in nature is really only an approximation to it. The interest in a human face, for example, lies just in the small points where the features are not symmetrical. (Study the portraits of the two girls reproduced opposite.)

Patterns from paper-folding and cutting to show one or two axes of symmetry were suggested in ❷ . Further activities in paper-folding can now be carried out. In these it is suggested that the children try to guess what shape will result before they open out the folded paper.

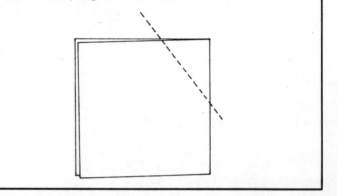

Fold a piece of paper as shown, so that the top edge fits on to itself. Cut off one corner as shown by the dotted line.
Take the corner you have cut off, and before you open it out guess what shape you will get. Open it out and see if you were right.
What name can you give to this shape?

With some children a useful discussion could take place about the angles and the sides of the resultant triangle.

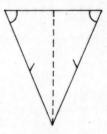

From their folding the children should be able to discover that the sides and angles marked are equal.

Similar assignments can be given for:
paper folded obliquely and cut as shown by the dotted line (guess the shape before opening).

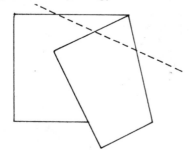

Paper folded in four with a right angle (guess before opening). Name the shape.
Can you cut off the corner so that you get a square?

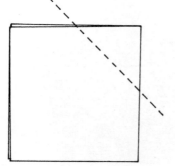

Paper folded in four with an oblique fold
This time there may be folds which are not axes of symmetry when the shape is opened out.
Mark in the axes of symmetry as before.

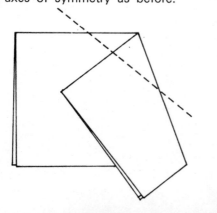

We can also look at the idea of symmetry in 3D objects. For instance, a brick could be 'cut' thus:

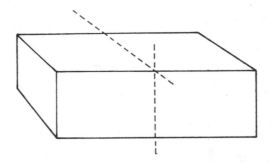

so that one half matches the other half. In this case we are not considering a line as in a 2D shape,

but a plane — a cut right through the brick. The brick, of course, has two other 'planes of symmetry'.

At this stage discovery will be largely by observation, and can be achieved both through natural objects, and through 3D geometrical shapes. For instance, some fruit such as apples, pears, tomatoes, can be cut to exhibit a plane of symmetry. Children can be asked to do this, and to look for examples outside the school, such as houses and other buildings.
With 3D shapes, plasticine or cheese is useful for cutting. In some cases it may be advisable for the teacher to prepare the shapes first.
The following activity is suitable for a group of children working together:

Each of you make a brick out of plasticine, so that the bricks look as nearly as possible the same shape and size.
Cut your brick in two so that one part matches the other.
Find how many ways you could do this.

Other shapes to be investigated in this way, by cutting, could include cubes, equilateral triangular prisms, cylinders, spheres, but some of these will have to be made by the teacher first.

We shall return to the symmetry of 3D shapes later by looking at the ways in which they can be replaced or fitted into 'holes'. But first we shall have a look at everyday objects and tile patterns again for rotational symmetry.

For the first activity a collection of tins with lids will be required. This should include a variety of interesting shapes, and should not be limited to regular shapes, e.g.

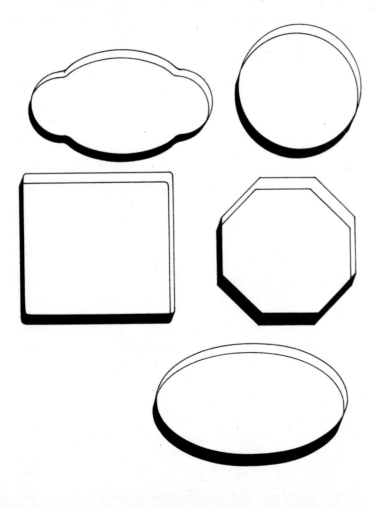

i Find out in how many ways each lid can be fitted on to its tin.
ii Trace round the edge of each lid on coloured paper. Cut out the shape. In how many ways can you fold each shape so that one half matches the other half ? Mark the creases clearly.
Is there sometimes a connection between the results you obtained in i and ii ?
Display your results.

Repeat this activity with regular shapes, either in coloured plastic material, or cut from card using a template. These shapes should include a square, equilateral triangle, pentagon, hexagon, octagon, etc. For each a 'frame' can be drawn round the shape to represent the tin, and the shape used as the 'lid', e.g.

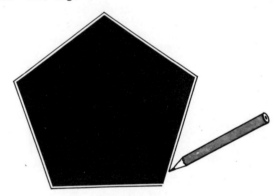

5 Tile patterns – tessellations

Patterns which use shapes to cover a plane surface (two-dimensional) without gaps or overlapping, i.e. which fill the plane, are called tessellations. These must not be confused with finding areas. When finding areas we are concerned with covering the surface enclosed by the boundary. When considering tessellations we shall not consider any boundary – we could go on and on making the pattern.

For the following activities a group of children working together will require at least twelve of each shape (these must be the same shape and size).

Suggested shapes (in plastic material or cardboard):

Triangles – equilateral, isosceles, any other triangles (congruent, of course).

Squares.

Quadrilaterals – rectangles, parallelograms, trapezia, irregular quadrilaterals including both.

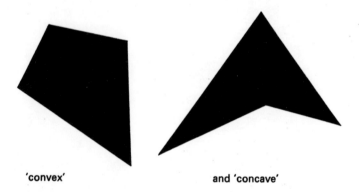

'convex'   and 'concave'

Regular pentagons, hexagons, octagons, etc.

> Take a collection of triangles of the same shape and size.
> See if you can fit them together to make a tile pattern so that there are no shapes overlapping, and no gaps between shapes.

Try similar activities with the other shapes. The children can make a list, or a display using coloured gummed-paper 'tiles', to show which shapes will fit in this way.

> When you have made a pattern with the shapes, see in how many ways you could lift one shape and replace it in its 'hole' in the pattern.
> Can you find any shapes which can be replaced in only one way; two ways; three ways; and so on?
> Try to explain your conclusions.

Children should be encouraged to look for interesting tessellations, such as floors, brickwork, wall tiles, and so on, and to make collections of pictures of their own sketches of these. For instance, the different patterns of brickwork associated with 'bonds' were mentioned in ▼. This might now be put as an assignment for outside school work this way, 'Where do you see tessellations of rectangles?' 'Is the same pattern used every time?'

> Make a tile pattern or tessellation using triangles of the same shape and size.
> Can you see any parallel lines?
> How many sets of parallel lines are there?

The above can be repeated using parallelograms, rhombuses and rectangles. A pattern can be started on squared paper and the children asked to continue the pattern, e.g.

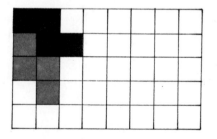

From triangle patterns, angles which fit together in threes to make two right angles can be seen, and reference to the activities with 'trellis work' given on pp. 9-10 will indicate the approach to this. Children can also be asked to find different quadrilaterals made from two triangles which appear in the triangle tessellations, and these can be picked out in colour as an extension of the pattern work.

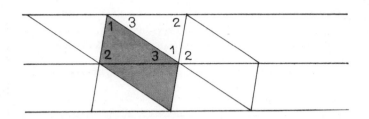

From their work with the 'trellis-work' and triangle patterns, children will have discovered that any number of angles together forming a 'straight angle' have the total measure of two right angles. This can be further investigated.

A supply of triangles of the same shape and size will be required. Although not essential, it is helpful if these can be in three colours — some red, some blue, some white, for instance.

> Mark the angles of the triangles 1, 2, 3 as shown in the diagram above.
> Fit the triangles together to make a tessellation or tile pattern.
> Which angles fit together to make a 'straight angle' or two right angles?
> Can you discover anything about the angles of a triangle from this?

This is one example showing that the sum of the angles of a triangle is two right angles. Other experiences illustrating this, and leading to the discovery of the angles of regular polygons, will come later.

Before considering this we shall take another look at angles, this time associated with turning.

6 Angles and turning

Up to this point most of the work on angles has been considered from 'corners' of shapes and little mention has been made of turning (except in connection with symmetry by rotation), or of angles as a measure of turn. But children will have experienced something of this in their activities with the clock and the movement of its hands, in their work with the compass and compass directions in geography and science, and in turning and movement in games and physical education. Their environment may also have included wheels on shafts, record-player turntables, roundabouts, even rotating searchlight beams. Activities leading to the measurement of the amount of turn can be introduced, first in terms of right angles and fractions of a complete turn, and later in degrees. Assuming that the compass directions N.S.E.W. are known in relation to the classroom, one suggestion for starting is:

Face North. Turn clockwise so that you face East.
How many right angles have you **turned** through?
Start by facing North again. Make one complete turn. Where are you facing now?
How many right angles did you turn through?
What fraction or part of a complete turn did you make to face East?

Teachers will be able to think of similar activities to bring in the other compass points, and fractions of a complete turn (e.g. ½ turn, ¾ turn).

Fold a 4-inch square of coloured gummed paper to make two creases at right angles. Mark North, South, East and West on the arms.
Fold again from corner to corner to get half right angles, and mark in NE, SE, SW, NW.
Mount the paper on card. Fix a pointer at the centre with a paper fastener.
Move the pointer to face North. Turn it clockwise to point to West. How many right angles have you **turned** through?
What fraction of a complete turn has the pointer moved through?

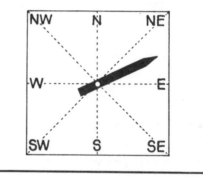

Other turns (in both directions) can be given, e.g.
'I faced West, then I turned anti-clockwise to South-East, so I turned through 1½ right angles.'

Angles as rotations can be further developed through the clock-face. The actual classroom clock, or the commercially produced cardboard clock-faces in use in many schools, are suitable for this. Or teachers may prefer paper-folding as suggested on p. 12.

The idea of measurement in degrees will have to be introduced by the teacher, and this could possibly be linked with history. Some children may be able to find references to this themselves in information books. One complete turn of the minute hand is made in one hour. One complete turn is divided into 360 degrees (written 360°). This can be compared with the year of the Ancient Egyptians and Babylonians. It is thought that they divided the circle into 360 equal parts because the year was believed to have 360 days – one degree for one day of the Sun's path round the Earth.

Start with the minute hand on 12. Move it round one complete turn.
How many right angles has it **turned** through?
How many degrees has it turned through?
How many degrees in one right angle? in two right angles?.....
and so on.
If the minute hand points to half-past, what will it point to if it turns through 90°?..... and so on.

What fraction or part of a complete turn does the minute hand turn through in five minutes?
Move the hand to help you if you wish.
How many degrees is this?
Start at 12 and move the minute hand five minutes at a time to 1, 2, 3, 4, ... and round to 12. Count the degrees as you go.

Some children may be able to attempt more difficult questions, e.g.
Start with the minute hand at quarter past. What will it point to if it turns through 120°?
How many degrees does the hour hand turn through in one hour?.... in 10 minutes?
The simplified protractor referred to on page 9 can be introduced at this stage for measuring angles, both in the clockwise and anti-clockwise directions.

This protractor is marked in 5° intervals with no numerals and can be used as illustrated.
Starting at A we count 5, 10, 15, 20, 25, 30, 35..... about 37 degrees.
This is sufficient at this stage and serves to emphasise the approximate nature of measurement.

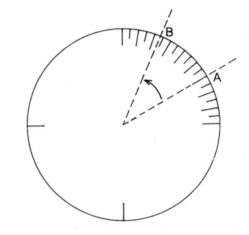

In the earlier work on tessellations using triangles one activity led to the idea that the sum of the angles of the triangle was two right angles. This might be looked on as a special case, and in the further activities on tessellations we shall want to use the general case that the sum of the angles of any triangle is two right angles (180°). Other suggestions to illustrate this are given below. They are not set out as assignments, teachers being left to produce their own when required.

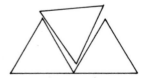

i fitting together equilateral triangles, e.g. plastic shapes, Toblerone packets, etc.

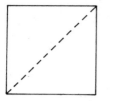

ii from symmetry of a square by folding.
4 right angles in the square. What about each triangle?

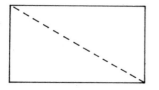

iii cutting a rectangle diagonally for a similar result.
4 right angles in the rectangle. What about each triangle?

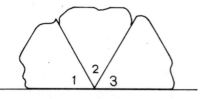

iv cut out large triangles in paper or thin card.
Tear off corners. Fit on to a straight line.

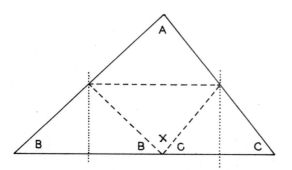

v fold a cut-out triangle as shown. Angles fit together at X.

vi triangles fitting as in tessellations.

From these (some of which include special cases such as equilateral triangles, and right-angled triangles) discussion can bring out that we can assume the general result for any triangle.

This discovery, that the sum of the angles of any triangle is two right angles, or 180°, can be used to find out more about the angles of polygons, and to look more closely at those shapes which will cover a plane surface without overlapping, or without leaving a gap.

This can be considered now.

7 More about polygons and tessellations

In the section on rigid and non-rigid 2D frameworks at the beginning of this guide it was found that the most economical way of obtaining rigidity for polygonal frameworks was to make triangles inside the shape by adding struts. For instance, a regular pentagon framework would have struts added like this,

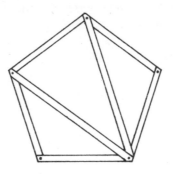

producing three triangles.

We can use this discovery and the one about the sum of the angles of a triangle to find the angles of regular polygons, and this can then be used in work on tessellations.

Templates of regular polygons will be required (equilateral triangle, square, pentagon, hexagon, octagon ..... and so on). Teachers should recall the earlier work on rigidity and adding struts to make triangles inside the shape.

Draw round the templates to make outlines of the shapes. Begin with the square. Start at one corner and draw a straight line to each of the other corners where this is possible.

How many lines can you draw? How many triangles have you made inside the square?
Now do the same for the other shapes.
What is the sum of the angles of a triangle?
Work out the sum of the angles of each shape, in right angles.
Put your results in a table like this:

number of sides	number of triangles	sum of angles (in right angles)
3	1	2
4	2	4
5	–	–
–	–	–
–	–	–

Will the above table also hold if the polygons are not regular?

With some children these results might be represented in graphical form,
e.g. number of sides; number of triangles,
number of sides; sum of angles in right angles.
The more able children may wish to look for a pattern in their results, and to work out the interior angle of regular polygons in degrees. These suggestions are not given as 'assignments' but indicated below for the teacher's information.
Regular polygons have sides of equal length, and angles of equal size. From the previous table an extended one can be made:

No. of sides	No. of triangles	Sum of angles (in rt.angles)	Sum of angles (in degrees)	Interior angle (in degrees)
3	1	2	180	60
4	2	4	360	90
5	3	6	540	108
6	4	8	720	120
7	5	10	900	$128\frac{4}{7}$
8	6	12	1080	135
—	—	—	—	—
—	—	—	—	—
—	—	—	—	—
n	$n-2$	$2(n-2)$ or $2n-4$	$2(n-2)\times 90$ or $(2n-4)\times 90$	$\dfrac{2(n-2)\times 90}{n}$

The interior angle can be obtained from the sum of the angles, e.g. a pentagon has five equal angles so the interior angle is obtained by dividing 540° by 5. Similarly the interior angle of an octagon is obtained by dividing 1080° by 8.

Although this is mainly for teachers' information, more able children who have experienced the measurement of angles in degrees can produce this table, and will spot the pattern in columns 2 and 3. The number of triangles formed is always two less than the number of sides of the polygon. Each triangle so formed within the shape has the sum of its angles as two right angles, so the sum of the angles of any polygon given in right angles is twice the number of triangles made, and this can be converted to degrees.

This information can be used when we look at tessellations, and see why some shapes will fit without overlapping or without a gap, while others will not. The following assignments show one possible development.

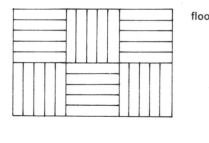

Look about the school, and elsewhere, for patterns of bricks, tiles, and floors.
Make sketches of some of these.
Which shapes were used in most of the patterns you found?

It is likely that squares and rectangles will be the most common shapes, although occasionally hexagonal tiles may be seen. In one school the following were discovered:

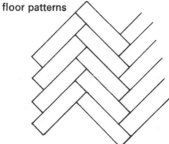

floor patterns

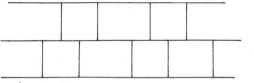

paving stones

brickwork

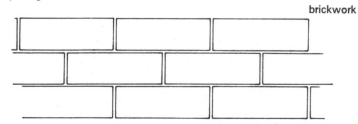

For the next activities a supply of plastic or cardboard shapes will be required (at least 6 of each; preferably a dozen or more) – triangles (any shape), quadrilaterals both convex and concave, regular pentagons, regular hexagons, regular octagons . . . . . and so on.

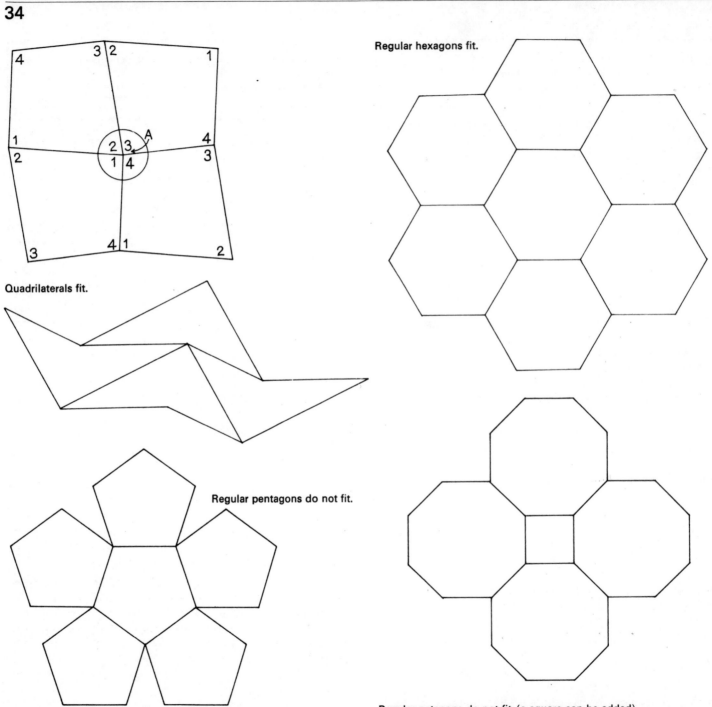

Quadrilaterals fit.

Regular hexagons fit.

Regular pentagons do not fit.

Regular octagons do not fit (a square can be added).

> Take the collection of triangles.
> See if these could be used as tiles to cover a surface without overlapping or without leaving a gap anywhere. Remember you are not concerned with the boundary or edges of the surface you are covering, but whether the triangles will fit together.
> Use what you know about the angles to explain why triangles can be used in this way.

At A, each of the three different angles appears twice, making a total of 360° (4 right angles).

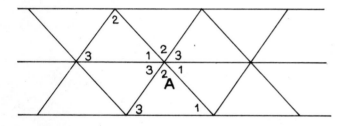

> Take a collection of each of the other shapes in turn and find which will make tessellations (tile patterns).
> Which shapes leave a gap?
> Can you find other shapes which you can fit into the spaces for those shapes which leave a gap?
> The following results may be discovered:

The more mathematically mature children can discuss the reasons for some shapes fitting, and others not. This might be approached this way:

> Mark the corners of your quadrilaterals 1, 2, 3, 4, or in four different colours, so that the marks are in the same place on each quadrilateral.
> Try to fit the shapes together to make a tessellation.
> What is the sum of the angles of a quadrilateral?
> Can you use this to say why the four corners fit together at one place?

Each of four different angles, shown 1, 2, 3, 4, or by the four different colours, occurs once at one point, and so the four angles make a total of 360°.
The other shapes can be investigated in a similar way.

> What is the sum of the angles of a regular pentagon?
> What is each angle of a pentagon (in degrees)?
> Can you explain why pentagons like these will not fit together?

The angle of a regular pentagon is 108°, and so at a point where three pentagons meet, the total is 324°. This leaves a gap of 36°.
Hexagons and octagons can be looked at in this way, teachers asking similar questions. The angle of a regular hexagon is 120°, so three of these will fit to make 360°. The angle of a regular octagon is 135°. Two fit together making 270°, so a square with 90° is needed to make 360°, as shown in the diagram opposite.

Having seen that regular pentagons do not 'fit', children may like to try and find if any pentagons can be used for tessellations. One result found by some 11-year-olds was the following:

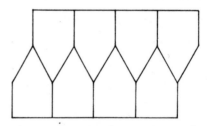

They were really using pentagons made from squares and equilateral triangles.
Other tessellations can be attempted using two shapes—for instance, squares and equilateral triangles, regular hexagons and equilateral triangles. Examples of patterns in tiles, fabrics, wallpaper, natural instances such as honeycombs, and so on can be collected and displayed, and the reasons why shapes like these fit together investigated.
The results of the activities found by actually moving tiles or plastic shapes, can often be better illustrated or recorded if the shapes are then cut out from coloured gummed paper and mounted. The reasons for some shapes fitting may also come out better in discussion between teacher and children than through set assignments.

A review of what has been done
Recapitulation of earlier work on parallel lines, with some further activities about angles associated with this.
An introduction to modular arithmetic through patterns on circles.

Symmetry
axes of symmetry, planes of symmetry, simple reflection and rotation.

Tessellations
fitting shapes together, and the link with rotation.

Angles
through turning, leading to measurement in right angles and as parts of a complete turn; and an introduction to measurement in degrees.

Another look at tessellations and the angles of polygons.

In all this the 'spiral' treatment can be seen. We keep coming back to earlier topics and developing them in a slightly more advanced way each time, thus showing progression.

Regular Octagons

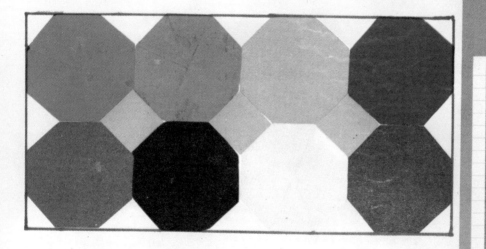

I made these octagons like this, first of all I got a piece of sticky paper and then folded it in half three times, and that left me with an isosceles triangle, then I measured one of the two shortest sides which was 2½ inches long. After I had done this I measured the same length on the longest side and put a dot there. Then from the top point I drew a line to the dot and cut that bit off. Then when I opened out the other piece there was an octagon left. Octagons will not fit exactly, there will always be a square left in the middle.

Irregular Pentagons....

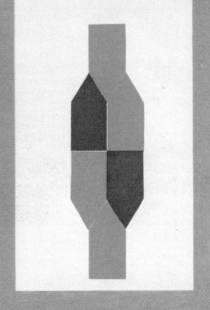

After I had cut some irregular pentagons out I stuck them on to a sheet of paper. To my surprise they fitted exactly, and I thought I had found a way of fitting irregular pentagons together exactly, then I stuck some more down and they did not fit. But then I found out why the first ones I stuck down fitted exactly. It's because I made one angle 144 degrees and there were 7 pentagons so all the degrees added up to 360°.

After I had cut out twelve irregular pentagons I got a sheet of paper and made a few patterns to see if they fitted together exactly and they did, this is how I made the irregular pentagons. First of all I got a piece of card and drew a line 1½" long and then I drew a line upwards on both sides of the first lines; I drew 2" long. Then I got a compass and set it to 1½" then I drew two lines and at the point where they met each other I drew two lines. These pentagons are not all irregular, they're only half irregular because 2 sides are the same length and the other 3 sides are the same length.

..will sometimes fit together.

Holymead Junior School.

THE REGULAR HEXAGON

Holymead Junior School

The Regular Pentagon

Overlapping Pentagons

I found only one way of overlapping pentagons corner to corner, the shape of the overlapping bit is called a Rhombus If you continually do it this way you will find that you are making yet another shape, this shape is called a Decagon.

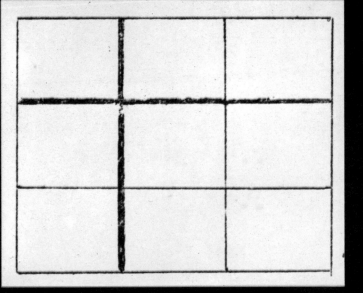

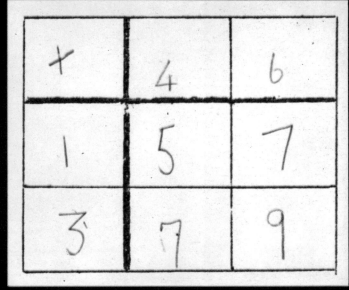

+	4	6
1	5	7
3	7	9

+	10	8 4
2	12	(6)
9	19	13

8 Tables

It has been suggested that children should construct tables other than the customary 'multiplication table'. These help to show links between apparently unrelated topics – and this is one of the main roles played by mathematics. It may be useful for a start to duplicate a number of blank forms and discuss with the children how these might be completed.

In the illustration opposite, for example, the rule for composition is addition, indicated by '+' in the top-left square. Free choice was allowed of numbers in the top border (4, 6) and the left-hand border (1, 3), but then the correct numbers had to be entered in the table itself, e.g. the '9' (in the second row and second column) is obtained by adding the 3 (the given number in the second row) and the 6 (the given number in the second column). Some children need plenty of practice in simply 'how the table works', e.g. 'The 6 belongs to the "2" row and the "4" column.'

Once the idea for completing the tables is established (and for many children this comes immediately), variations can be introduced. The following is an excerpt from *Computation and Structure* ❷ , pp. 78, 81.

We can construct a table of even and odd numbers to show this:

+	E	O
E	E	O
O	O	E

This table is interpreted as follows:

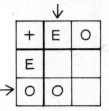

E stands for 'even', O stands for 'odd'.

When we add an odd number (indicated by the horizontal arrow at O) and another odd number (indicated by the vertical arrow) then the result is even, and this is recorded by inserting an E (for even) where the row of the first arrow meets the column of the second.

This entry shows that the result of adding an odd number and an even one is an *odd* number, and similarly for the other entries.

These results can be useful to children when adding numbers, e.g. 2+10+6, they should then know that the sum of these will be even, and this provides a check for their work.

Some 10-year-olds ('not particularly mathematically gifted') had been studying symmetry and made half a letter 'A' which could swing round on a hinge so that it was either 'facing right' or 'facing left'.

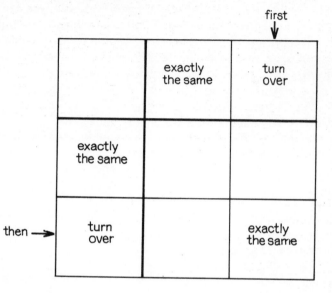

'facing right'   'facing left'

The half-A could be either 'left exactly as it is' or 'turned over', and the children made a table.

	exactly the same	turn over
exactly the same	exactly the same	turn over
turn over	turn over	exactly the same

This table was interpreted, for example, as 'turn over' and then 'turn over' again, giving the same effect as 'stay in exactly the same position'.

first ↓

	exactly the same	turn over
exactly the same		
turn over (then →)		exactly the same

The children suddenly started talking excitedly about the 'E and O' (even and odd) table mentioned above which, as it turned out, they had seen the previous week on television. They reproduced this table as well as the 'half-A' one and said that they were 'the same'. The following conversation ensued :

M. Can you tell me about this ?
V. We had a picture of half an A. On the other side of the paper there is another half an A. We made a table. We started off and when we finished it was the same as this [pointing to the odds and evens].
M. How did it look like the other one ?
V. Instead of having E and O we had the first letters.
M. How are the patterns the same ?
V. If you take the first letter it becomes the same. It is similar because it is the same sort of pattern. You have got the odds and evens. Evens that way and odds that way [pointing diagonally across the table]; 'Exactly the same' that way and 'Over' that way.

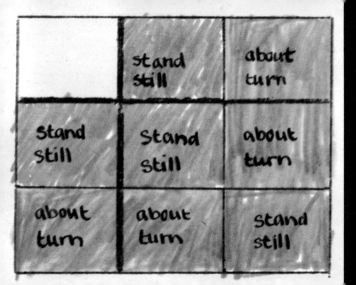

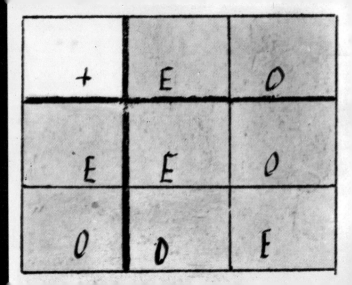

	Full turn	half turn
Full turn	full turn	half turn
half turn	half turn	full turn

This chart is about the hands on the clock.
A half turn and a full turn makes a half turn.
and a full turn and a full turn makes a full turn.
A half turn and a half turn makes a full turn.

Another group, of 9-year-old children, discussed with their teacher the effects of the orders 'Stand still' and 'About turn' (for example, 'About turn' followed by another 'About turn' gave the same **result** as simply 'Stand still'). The teacher filled in the table very roughly and the children again pointed out that it was the 'same' as the E and O table, which they had also seen on television. They demonstrated this 'sameness' by colouring E and 'Stand still' in orange; O and 'About turn' in green.

A search for other situations produced much discussion (e.g. 'repeat' and 'flip' for a gramophone record). Two members of the group were searching round the room, determined not to be outdone, when they came across a toy clock-face whose wooden hands were mercifully locked together.

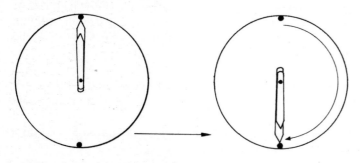

half turn top to bottom

They experimented with 'half turns' ('top to bottom' or 'bottom to top') and 'full turns' (all the way round, either 'top to top' or 'bottom to bottom') and came up, quite unaided, with the table reproduced opposite, suitably coloured.

Six weeks later, these children were able to recall the whole sequence: they had made their own discovery. They had, in fact, discovered for themselves 'modulo 2 arithmetic' (cf. p. 11 above), which we recall from *Computation and Structure* ❷ , pp. 89-90:

One of the developments in mathematics over the past century has been the introduction of different 'arithmetics' — we are not always concerned with the numbers 1, 2, 3, 4, 5, 6, 7, 8, 9, 10, 11, 12, 13, 14, 15, . . . but, perhaps with a different set, as for example with the clock which uses only twelve distinct numbers. A digital computer can in effect use only two numerals 0 ('off') and 1 ('on') and we end here with an 'arithmetic' associated with it, namely 'modulo 2'. Our 'clock' now is particularly simple.

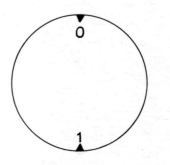

Starting from 0, one hour (say) is recorded as 1 and two hours by returning to 0 again, so that counting would be recorded by the crude 'clock' as follows:

0	1	2	3	4	5	6	7	8	9 ...

'mod. 2'	0	1	0	1	0	1	0	1	0	1 ...

even odd even odd even odd even odd even odd

The 'addition' table is particularly simple.

+ (mod 2)	0	1
0	0	1
1	1	0

It is no coincidence that this pattern is like that for 'even' and 'odd' (p. 78). In fact those numbers represented by 0 (modulo 2) are *even* and those represented by 1 (modulo 2) are *odd*.

9 Another look at rotational symmetry

In the introduction to *Shape and Size* ❷ a brief mention was made of the transformations of reflection, rotation, and translation, and how under these the shape and size of any figure are invariant.

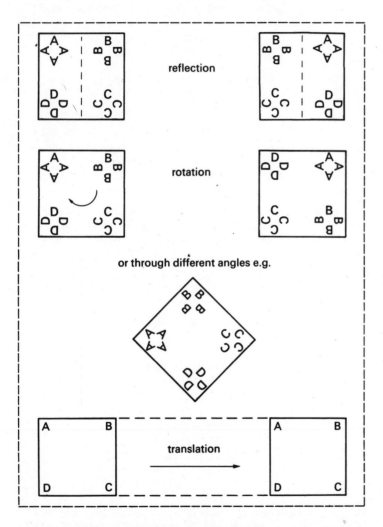

reflection

rotation

or through different angles e.g.

translation

Initial experience in these transformations was given through patterns arising in activities such as artwork, and through observation of patterns seen in tiling, brickwork and wall-

paper. Reflection and rotation were also associated with symmetry — reflection through such things as 'blot patterns', and rotation through finding the ways in which square and rectangular tiles could be replaced in their 'holes'. This was further investigated in the activities described earlier in this guide.

We shall now develop the idea of rotational symmetry as outlined in the introduction to *Shape and Size* ❷ .
First we shall consider rotation only, that is, without turning over the shape. This has already been touched on briefly on p. 26 of this guide, and the activities suggested there can be used as a starting-point.

The collection of tins and lids, and the regular shapes in frames, suggested on p. 26, can be used again. Teachers should recall the results of these activities, either by questioning and discussion, or where necessary, by actually allowing the children to repeat the activities. The ideas to be recalled are:

In how many ways can a lid be placed on its tin?
(This is particularly useful as we are not concerned with turning over yet.)
In how many ways can each regular shape be fitted into its frame? (No turning over).
Of particular interest will be the number of ways in which a circular lid can be placed on its tin, or the number of ways a sink-plug can be fitted into its hole.

If we take a simple shape such as a rectangular-shaped lid we see that it can be placed on its tin in two positions:

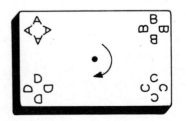

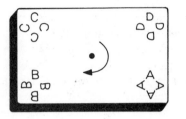

There are two movements or operations we can do on the lid. The first is to place it on its tin and 'leave it as it is', or 'stay put'. The operation is, 'leave it as it is'. As nothing has moved we can call this the 'neutral' operation, and denote it by N. The other movement or operation is to lift the lid from its position and turn it through two right angles (180°) about a point at its centre, and replace it on the tin. As it has turned through **two** right angles we might call this operation R_2. If we were to turn the lid through four right angles (360°) from any position it would result in this same position again, so in fact this movement is **not** a new operation. There are, then, two operations we can perform on it – N, 'stay put', or 'leave it as it is', and R_2, 'turn through 180°'.

We shall now see what happens if we combine two operations, that is, do one and then follow it by another operation or movement. There are four possible combinations of two operations. (Reference to the diagram of the rectangle above will help teachers to follow the operations.)

(i) Operation N, followed by operation N, means 'leave it as it is' followed by 'leave it as it is', and obviously the position will be unchanged.

(ii) Operation N, followed by operation R_2, means 'leave it as it is' and then 'turn through 180°'. This gives the same position as just turning through 180° (as R_2 on its own).

(iii) Operation R_2, followed by operation N, means 'turn through 180°' and then 'stay put'. Again this gives the same position as turning through 180° (as R_2 on its own).

(iv) Operation R_2, followed by operation R_2, means 'turn through 180°' and then 'turn through another 180°', which brings it back to the starting position. This means we arrive at the same position as doing movement or operation 'N' as if the rectangle was made to 'stay put' or if we 'leave it as it is'.

The above sequence of operations and the resultant positions can be recorded in table form:

	1st operation	
and then	N	R_2
N	N	R_2
R_2	R_2	N

2nd operation

As an example: the table shows R_2 'and then' R_2 again giving the same position as doing operation N.

Suitable colouring will show that this pattern is the 'same' as those in the previous section.

An assignment is given below on the rotation of a square in its frame (without 'turning over'). Teachers can then make up similar instructions for the rectangle (see above), parallelogram, equilateral triangle, and possibly the regular hexagon. The instructions are given in some detail for this first 'assignment', but subsequent ones need not be quite so detailed.

A square of plastic or cardboard, with sides about six inches, will be required.

Draw a frame round the square on a sheet of paper. Mark the corners of the square A, B, C, D, as shown, or colour them red, blue, green, yellow. This will help you to see the different positions of the squares.

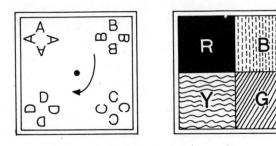

In how many ways can you fit the square into the frame?
What angle do you turn the square through each time you move it to a new position in the frame?
Place the square in this position in the frame.
Call it position 1.

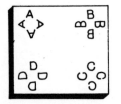

Turn the square in the frame without turning it over:
(i) turn it through one right angle clockwise. Call this position 2;
(ii) turn it through another right angle clockwise. How many right angles from the starting-point is this? Call this position 3;
(iii) turn it through another right angle clockwise. Call this position 4.
How many right angles from where you started have you turned the square?
(iv) Again, turn the square through one more right angle clockwise. Which position are you in now?
How many right angles has the square turned through?
Turning through four right angles produces the same result, the same position, as something else. What?
Make a drawing of the four positions:

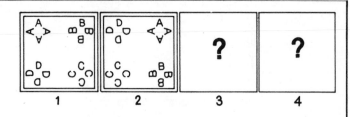

Now look at the movements, the things you did to the square. We call these **operations**. There are four:
(i) The first is 'leave the square as it is', or 'unchanged', or 'stay put'. You could call it 'do nothing'. Give it the letter N (for neutral).
(ii) Turning through **one** right angle (90°) from any position. Call this R_1.
(iii) Turning through **two** right angles (180°) from any position. Call this R_2.
(iv) Turning through **three** right angles (270°) from any position. Call this R_3.
We do not need a special name for turning through **four** right angles (360°). Why?

Now see what happens if you do **two** operations or movements, that is, do one operation and then follow it with another operation. Find the final position of the square when you do this. Actually move the square in its frame to help you to see what is happening. Here is one done for you:

Operation N followed by operation R_2 means: start, for example, in position 1 and then turn the square through **two** right angles (180°) clockwise. This brings the square to position 3. Now start at another position and do the two movements. What do you notice about the position where the square finishes?

Try this one: start in the position 1 again. Do operation R_2 followed by operation R_3. This means: turn the square through **two** right angles clockwise, and then turn it through another **three** right angles clockwise. Which position is the square in now? Try this starting at another position. Operation R_2 followed by operation R_3 gives the same position as doing operation ... ?

Do some more and find the position of the square each time:
R₁ followed by R₃
R₃ followed by R₂
R₂ followed by N
N- followed by N, and so on.

Start in different positions and record the single operation which would lead to the same position as doing the two operations.
Make a table like this :
N, R₁, R₂, R₃ along the top stand for the operations you do first.
N, R₁, R₂, R₃ down the left-side stand for the second operation.
The single operations which give the same position as doing two are written in the spaces. The two examples from above have been done for you:
N followed by R₂ gives the same position as doing operation R₂ on its own, indicated by the arrows.
R₂ followed by R₃ gives the same position as doing operation R₁ on its own, indicated by the arrows.
Try to complete the table. You may use your square to help you if you wish.

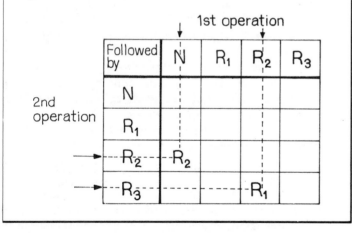

Turning over
We can now extend the operations on shapes to include turning over. This, of course, cannot be done with a tin lid, or a tile with one surface coloured. But there are tiles which can be turned over before being replaced, and other examples in everyday life afford useful starting-points. For instance, children can find how many ways a glazier could fit a rectangular pane of glass into its frame. They can be asked to consider this by looking at an actual window.
The more formal operations can be approached as follows:
(i) Cut out a rectangle from card. Mark its corners on both sides.
(ii) Use a rectangular-shaped piece of clear acetate sheet. Mark the corners. The marks can be seen from both sides.

What way could the corners be marked ? A similar marking to that for the previous activities could be used.

or reference to the symmetry of letters already discussed on p. 23 could bring out the fact that we could use HIOX. Why these four letters ? Are there any shapes we could use which would look the same from both sides when the rectangle is turned over and turned round about a point at the centre ? (e.g. — × ○ +). Are there any others ?
The window frame or 'hole' is shown below :

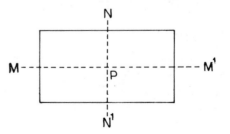

The fundamental mathematical idea of a **group** is behind the tables of the last two sections. The teacher who is interested in this is referred to the Appendix of this guide.

If we start with the rectangle in this position

it can be fitted into the frame in any one of the following positions:

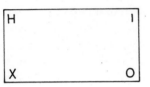

leave it as it is

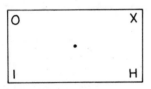

rotate through 180° about point P

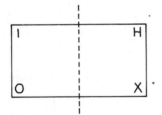

turn over about NN'

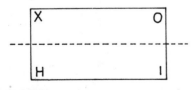

turn over about MM'

Discussion of fitting the rectangle into its frame in these ways can bring out some of the properties of rectangles, e.g. opposite edges are the same length, opposite angles are equal, and all four angles are equal (right angles.) Also the diagonals are equal.

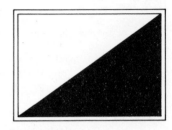

(The rectangle still fits its frame when rotated.)

As before we can indicate the movements or operations by letters. For instance we could use:

N for 'leave it as it is' or 'stay put'

R_2 for 'turn through 180° about P' or 'turn round'

V for 'turn over about NN' (about a **V**ertical line)'

H for 'turn over about MM' (about a **H**orizontal line)';

or we could use 0, 1, 2, 3 for the above operations in the same sequence.

A suggested 'assignment' for operations on a square was given on pp. 50-51. Teachers can make up similar activities for the rectangular window being replaced in its frame, using the notation given above.

Children should find out what happens if they carry out two or more of the movements or operations, one after the other. They can start in the original position shown above, and see what happens when they do one operation followed by another. What position results? Can they find **one** operation which produces the same position as the two? Repeat these activities starting at different positions. The result to look for is two operations which give the same position as doing one on its own, e.g. doing operation R_2 followed by operation H means 'turn the rectangle through 180° about P, then turn it over about a horizontal line MM''. Check the position of the letters at the corners compared with the position in which the rectangle was at the start. The position which results is the same position as doing operation V on its own (turning over about a vertical line from the starting position).

If the other notation was used (0, 1, 2, 3), 1 followed by 3 gives the same position as doing 2. Try all the combinations of two movements you can think of (16). As for the square, the results can be represented in table form.

1st Movement

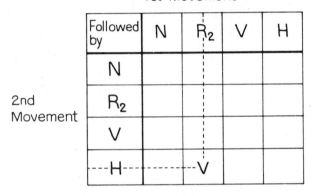

2nd Movement	Followed by	N	R₂	V	H
	N				
	R₂				
	V				
	H		V		

Or

1st Movement

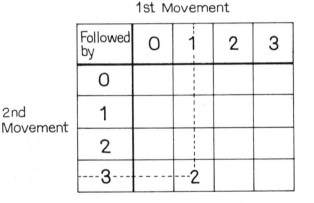

2nd Movement	Followed by	0	1	2	3
	0				
	1				
	2				
	3		2		

When presenting this to children an 'assignment card' similar to that for the square can be produced, or the teacher may find it easier to **discuss** the movements or operations with a small group of children and give a start this way, allowing the children to discover and record the results for themselves.

On p.48 it was recalled that shapes or geometrical figures were unchanged under certain transformations. The transformations which allowed movement in a plane without distortion of the shape were reflection, rotation, and translation. We have investigated what happens when two rotations about the same point are combined. Let us now look at combining reflections. In ▼ reflection was observed through patterns produced by paper-folding or by 'blot patterns'; earlier in this guide letters of the alphabet and shapes such as squares and rectangles were used as starting-points for activities on reflection. We saw that reflection leaves one line in the plane invariant and that this line acts as a 'mirror'. In the work on letters, patterns, and shapes we called this line an axis of symmetry. In some cases where we start with a shape on one side of the line and copy its 'reflection' on the other side we could think of this line as an 'axis of reflection'. Reflection can be investigated with tracing paper.

You will need a sheet of tracing paper. Make a drawing such as a triangle, a flag, or other simple shape near one corner of the paper.

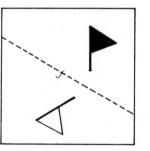

Make a fold near to your drawing as shown by the dotted line. This is an axis of reflection. Trace firmly over your shape so that an impression is made on the bottom paper. Open your fold. Go over the impression in pencil so that it shows clearly. Write down all the things you notice about the two shapes.

When considering combined rotations of a square about a point as suggested on pp. 50-51, it was discovered that the order of doing operations did not matter – the order could be interchanged. This illustrated the commutative property. It is interesting to see whether the same applies for reflection, and to see whether the order of operation matters when an object is reflected twice. Tracing paper can be used again, and folded to give axes of reflection.

A sheet of tracing paper, a pencil and two different coloured pencils are required:

Here is an example of an operation ('reflect in a line') which is not **commutative** (cf. p. 65). Children might like to think of everyday instances when the order of doing things does matter, and when it does not matter (e.g. dressing, putting on socks and shoes, washing dishes and drying them).

Make a simple drawing in ordinary pencil as you did before, and fold the paper to make an axis of reflection, AB. Trace over your shape. Open the paper and colour in the new outline impression of the shape. Now make a second fold like that marked CD.

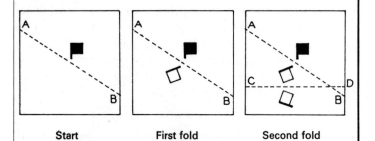

| Start | First fold | Second fold |

Press over your coloured shape so that it makes an impression on the bottom paper. Open your paper and use the same colour to go over this new impression of the shape.

Now use a different colour but reverse the order of your tracing.
You will need a larger piece of paper.
This time fold along CD and press over your first shape – the one in ordinary pencil. Open the paper and colour the outline of the impression. Now fold along the line AB and trace over the coloured shape to make an impression underneath. Open your paper and colour this impression.

Is it in the same **place** as the coloured shape produced in the first activity?
Does it matter in which order you fold the paper? If you combine two reflections do you get the same result if you change the order?

10 Polyhedra

In this section we shall have another look at 3D shapes, or solids. Sometimes these are called **polyhedra**, which means 'having many faces'. The idea of a solid implies a solid mass of material, but we shall be making shapes such as the cube either from card to give the outside surface, or from rods or straws to give a framework. Far too many books give detailed instructions on how to make the common 3D shapes from card, or stiff paper, and this results in children doing little more than copying 'nets' of these shapes. Certainly 'nets' may be useful for making some of the more difficult shapes, but this should not be the starting-point. It is better, perhaps, to start with a simple shape such as a cube and ask the children to look at it carefully from all directions, and then to construct their own cube from card. This can be tackled at first by cutting out six squares and joining these with Sellotape to make a cube shape. From this starting-point children can try to arrange six similar squares joined with Sellotape to form a 'flat shape' as shown below, so that they make a 'net' which can be folded to form the cube.

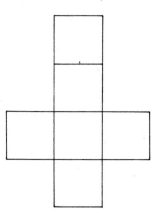

Identical cardboard boxes of cuboid shape can be provided, one of which is left as a box and the other opened out. An examination of such a box, for instance, will assist the children in seeing that there is a way of folding to make a solid shape.

A typical 'assignment' using squares to make a cube might be:

Use the six squares of card (or plastic) and Sellotape to make a cube. When you have finished open it out again without removing all the Sellotape so that the six squares lie flat on the table.

See if you can fold it up again to make a cube. Now use the squares again, and try to arrange them in a different pattern so that they will again make a cube when folded round.

In how many different ways can you arrange the six squares to make a cube when folded round? Copy some of the arrangements on to squared paper to make 'nets' for cubes.
Cut them out and fold them to make cubes. You may have to add small tabs to some edges to stick the cube together.

Similar assignments can be given using four equilateral triangles which can be stuck together to make the polyhedron shown below, which is called a 'regular tetrahedron'.

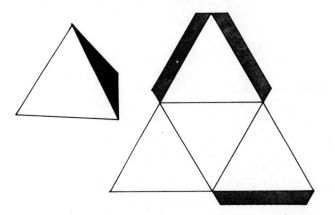

'Net' for regular tetrahedron. The shaded portions show possible portions for small tabs.

As with the cube the first approach should be largely experimental, the children trying to devise their own ways of making the shape. From their attempts discussion can lead to a suitable 'net' which could be used.

Another method of construction is to make a framework of the cube and tetrahedron using milk straws cut in half and joined at the corners (or vertices) by small pieces of pipe cleaner. With such a construction the faces of the shapes must be imagined. An alternative method is to use dowel rods with small rings at each end through which paper fasteners can be pushed to make a joint. These have the advantage of being more rigid than straws.

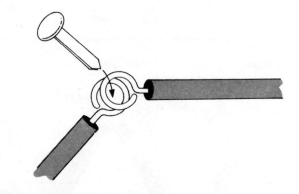

Paper fastener pushed through both rings

While the making of these shapes itself is valuable, we should not stop at the construction but investigate the shapes to find mathematical relationships. There are five regular polyhedra which can be used for this in the first instance. Two, the cube and tetrahedron, are within the capability of children to construct. The other three are shown below together with their 'nets'. These may be beyond most children to construct and teachers may have to provide their own models.

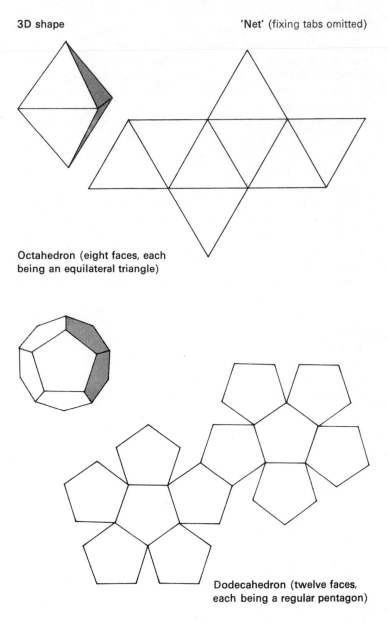

3D shape   'Net' (fixing tabs omitted)

Octahedron (eight faces, each being an equilateral triangle)

Dodecahedron (twelve faces, each being a regular pentagon)

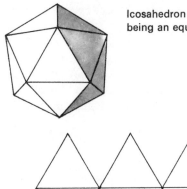

Icosahedron (twenty faces, each being an equilateral triangle)

Isometric or 'triangle' paper is also useful for those shapes which have equilateral faces, and this can be obtained from most educational stationers.

An interesting activity once the polyhedra have been made is to see if there is any relationship between the faces, edges, and vertices (corners). Reference to *Shape and Size* ▼, p. 12 will remind teachers of these terms.

Plastic shapes of the regular pentagon, and equilateral triangle, can be used as templates for drawing 'nets', or a pentagon template can be made by tying a single knot in a strip of paper, say $1\frac{1}{2}$ inches wide, as shown here:

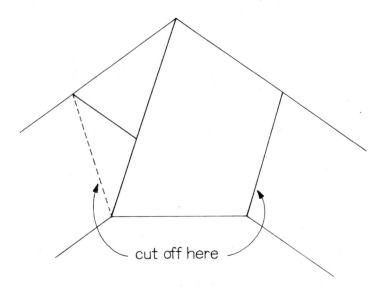

cut off here

Can you find anything interesting about these shapes? Count the faces, edges, and vertices and see what you discover.

Make a table to help you find a relationship.

shape	number of faces (F)	number of vertices (V)	number of edges (E)
tetrahedron	4	4	6
cube	6		
octahedron	8		
....			
....			
....			

Look at the numbers and see if you can find a pattern.

Discussion of the results may help the children discover Euler's theorem

$$F + V = E + 2.$$

The five regular polyhedra investigated so far were recognised by Euclid some two thousand years ago. But we should not limit our activities to these, and children can use similar methods of construction for making other solid shapes. Squares, rectangles, isosceles triangles, and so on can be used to make cuboid shapes, various pyramids, and prisms, or straws and pipe cleaners used to make framework representations of them, and then children can try to discover whether Euler's formula applies to these, too.

Solid shapes made from card can be made to look attractive by colouring the faces and this can also provide an interesting mathematical diversion.

When you have made some shapes from card, colour the faces. Paint or crayon the faces using different colours so that no two faces which are adjacent (next to each other) have the same colour.

Another 'diversion' which children may find interesting is to make shapes such as a cube out of clay, to press in the faces to form 'dimples' and to see if any relationships discovered for the polyhedra have analogues for these. Irregular shaped stones which have faces and points may also be used in this activity. For instance where we counted faces, edges, and vertices for polyhedra we can look for 'valleys, ridges, and mountains' on the stones.

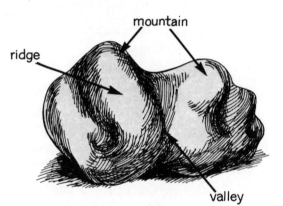

A similar investigation can be carried out on a spherical object such as a large ball. If lines are drawn on the surface (the diagram shows one such possibility), this is divided into 'regions'. The lines can be considered as 'arcs', and where these meet we have 'corners' or 'vertices'. Again we can see if there is any relationship between 'regions', 'arcs', and 'corners' and compare this with the relationships discovered for polyhedra.

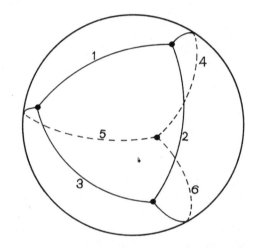

Some footballs and other 'games' balls have their cases made from panels. These provide ready-made examples of 'regions', 'arcs', and 'corners'.

For example, in the above diagram, we have:

Regions	Corners	Arcs
4	4	6

and $R + C - A = 2$.

Again, taking the equator and one meridian on a globe,

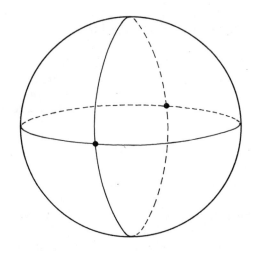

the number of regions is 4, the number of corners (where the 'lines' meet) is 2 and the number of arcs is 4. (The equator, for example, is partitioned into two arcs through meeting the meridian.) So once again

R + C — A = 4 + 2 — 4 = 2.

Teachers wishing to find other methods of constructing polyhedra, and other information on such shapes, will find *Mathematical Models* by Cundy and Rollett (O.U.P.), a useful book.

11 Back to transformations

In *Shape and Size* ⚈ and again on p. 48 of this guide, reference was made to the transformations of reflection, rotation, and translation. So far most of the activities on these have been concerned with reflection and rotation. Let us now look at translation. Already we have seen in ⚈ how this occurs frequently in children's patterns made with potato prints, lino prints, or stencils, and can be observed in the familiar repeating pattern in wallpaper. As a reminder of this, children can study patterns made from potato prints, etc. and wallpapers, find the basic motif or shape and discover how this 'moves' along the pattern. When such a shape is moved without being turned at all so that each print moves the same distance in the same direction we say it is subject to a **translation**. Reference to *Shape and Size* ⚈ , pp. 8 and 56, will recall this.

Children can investigate translation in another way by actually moving or 'translating' themselves to different positions, and through this see the possibilities of combining two or more translations in a similar way to discovering about combining rotations and reflections. This activity can be carried out in the school hall or in the playground and is suitable for group work suggested verbally by the teacher rather than by assignment cards, although teachers who wish to use the latter might well compile them from the suggestions outlined below.

Work in pairs. Mark two points with chalk on the floor or playground at least 20 yards apart (indicated by A and B in the diagram). One child is then set the task of walking from A along two 'straight' lines, i.e. in two directions so as to reach B. His partner can trace these with chalk, e.g.

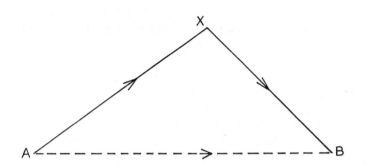

They then go back to A and are asked to see if they can walk along **one** 'straight' line (in one direction) from A so that they arrive at the same position, B, as they did after walking along two lines. In the diagram this is shown by the dotted line AB. Other 'walks' in a similar fashion can be undertaken by pairs of children. From this activity the teacher can bring out the idea that here we have one **translation** which results in the same position as doing two successive translations (i.e. first A to X and then X to B).

If we think about the ideas of group structure introduced in the activities on reflection and rotation, similar questions can be asked of the children, without introducing any formal discussion about groups, e.g.

'Is there anything we could do which would make no difference to the position we arrived at after one movement or translation?' The immediate response may well be, 'No', but if the operations on the square and rectangle are recalled, children may be led to see that again we can have as an operation, 'Do nothing' or 'Stay put'.
'Is there any translation which will return to your starting-point?' (e.g. after moving from A to X we could return to A along the same path).

As with some of the other work outlined in this guide it is interesting to provide other activities which can be looked upon as 'diversions'. With 'translations' of themselves across the hall or playground the children could be asked to find in how many ways, walking in straight lines, they could go from A to B. A variety of answers will result and discussion can show that there is no limit to the paths that could be used. This might be compared with the number of ways that a circular lid can be placed on its tin.

Having carried out activities that involve reflection, rotation, and translation, some children may like to investigate patterns which use all three transformations. These are sometimes called **isometries** — transformations which take any shape or figure into a position where its size and shape are unchanged. One such investigation can be derived from making patterns (potato or lino prints, or stencils) and a study of wallpaper patterns.

At this point we can use the pattern-making activities first encountered in ❼ to make a more detailed study of some aspects of symmetry. This can be done through strip patterns, using some method of printing (potato, lino, stencil) to make the basic motif. Assignment cards may not be necessary for such activities, the teacher instead starting off a group of children with simple instructions on how to begin the pattern. When the pattern is finished the children in the group can be brought together to study each other's patterns, to look for the basic motif and to find out how it was repeated on the strip — by reflection, or rotation, combined with translation; or by combinations of reflection and rotation with translation. To enable teachers to see the possibilities of such an activity a more detailed account is given below. But it is not suggested that it be presented to children in this form. The examples below give the basic ideas for teachers' information. Teachers should decide for themselves the most suitable form of presentation.

A shape must be chosen for the print or stencil. This will be repeated or translated along a narrow strip of paper to give a **repeating** pattern. At this stage we are concerned only with 'frieze' patterns along a strip and not 'all-over' patterns covering a whole plane. A suitable starting-point might be to use a strip of paper about 3 inches wide and about a yard long. This can be folded several times to produce lines and rectangular spaces which are useful guides for making the repeating pattern:

e.g.

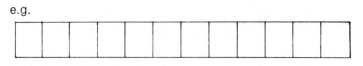

The shape which is to be used to produce the pattern should not be symmetrical, as this makes it difficult to follow some of the reflections and rotations in the overall strip pattern. Any shape or design can be used. It can be irregular or 'geometrical' (such as a triangle). For simplicity a 'flag' is shown here cut as a stencil:

Having decided on the motif or shape for the pattern the children use this to make a **repeating** pattern along the strip. They can do this in any way they wish provided that care is taken to ensure that it is a repeating pattern in some form. The patterns should then be studied to see if they fall into any of the categories illustrated below.

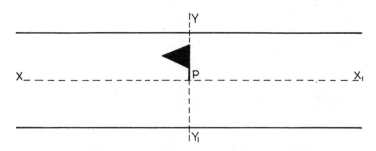

So that patterns can be followed we consider two directions— the line XX¹ parallel to the length of the strip, and the line YY¹ perpendicular to the length of the strip. These will help us to consider reflections. The basic motif (the flag) can also be rotated through 180° about the point P. In each of the patterns given below there is a translation as well, the motif or shape being moved along the strip to produce the repeat.

1

Translation only

2

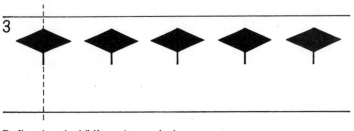

Reflection in XX¹ and translation

3

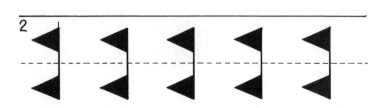

Reflection in YY¹ and translation

4

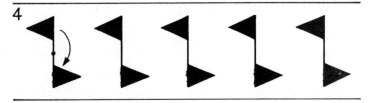

Rotation through 180° about P and translation

5

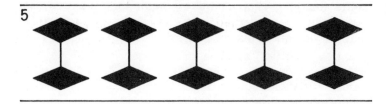

Rotate (2) through 180° about P, or rotate (3) through 180° about P, or reflect (2) in YY¹ — each followed by translation

6

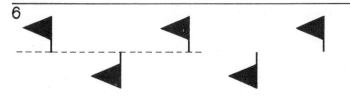

Translate half the distance used in (1) then follow by a reflection in XX¹

7

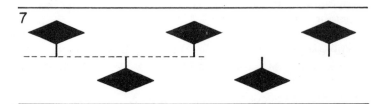

Pattern (3) translated half the distance and followed by a reflection in XX¹

The patterns shown above are relatively easy to follow. More difficult ones can arise from considering different positions of the lines for reflections, and the point for rotating, in relation to the basic motif or shape. Overlapping may also occur with different distances of translation for examples (6) and (7). It is best, therefore, to try at this stage to limit the study to easily recognisable examples. But, even with added difficulties of overlapping, and no matter how complicated the basic motif, each proper repeating pattern on a strip reduces to one of the **seven examples above**.

As an extension of this, children can study and discuss border patterns on wallpaper and try to discover into which of the seven types the pattern falls. Here the teacher may have to point out that the basic shape of the pattern need not be a single shape as with the stencil.

For example:

Basic pattern
This basic pattern could produce this for type (1):

i

or this for (1):

ii

i used to give type (5) will give a simple pattern but ii used to give type (5) can produce quite a complicated pattern which might be difficult to analyse.

Nevertheless all the above activities can give valuable experience in recognising the transformations of reflection, rotation, and translation, and discovering combinations of these, in an informal way.

Appendix

Tables arising from quite different activities have been seen to have the same 'pattern' (cf. p. 44). For instance, the table on p. 51, when completed, would look like this:

1st operation

	N	R_1	R_2	R_3
N	N	R_1	R_2	R_3
R_1	R_1	R_2	R_3	N
R_2	R_2	R_3	N	R_1
R_3	R_3	N	R_1	R_2

Followed by — top; 2nd operation — left

and this has the same structure as that for addition modulo 4:

+	0	1	2	3
0	0	1	2	3
1	1	2	3	0
2	2	3	0	1
3	3	0	1	2

Referring to the first of these tables, several interesting things emerge:

i Combining any two operations gives the same result as some particular single operation, e.g. R_2 followed by R_3 is the same as doing R_1 on its own. Each operation may be considered as an 'element' of the set of (four) operations; we can then express the previous sentence by saying that combining two elements gives another element of the set.

ii If we take a sequence of three elements it does not matter at which end we start, e.g.
(a) (R_2 followed by R_3) and then followed by R_1 produces the same result as
(b) R_2 followed by (R_3 followed by R_1).
(a) (R_2 followed by R_3) gives R_1. This followed by R_1 gives R_2.
(b) (R_3 followed by R_1) gives N. So R_2 followed by N gives R_2.

This illustrates the **associative** property, see below and *Computation and Structure* ❷.

iii There is one particular or unique element (operation) which has the property that it does not change any element (operation) of the set with which it is combined. In this case it is the operation 'leave it as it is', operation N, e.g. operation N combined with R_2 gives the same result as R_2 combined with N, and the same result as R_2 on its own. This element N is called the **neutral** or **identity** element.

iv Every element has an **inverse**, that is, for **every** element (operation) there is **one** element (operation) which 'undoes' it, and returns it to the position we started with (like the neutral operation), e.g.
R_2 followed by R_2 results in the same position as the neutral operation, so R_2 is the **inverse** of R_2.
R_3 followed by R_1 results in the same position as the neutral operation, so R_1 is the **inverse** of R_3. Similarly R_3 is the **inverse** of R_1.
If a set has associated with it a rule of combination with the properties shown at (i), (ii), (iii) and (iv) above it is said to be a **group** in the mathematical sense. Briefly the properties are:

Closure: combining two elements gives another element of the set (in the above case combining two operations produced the same result as one operation).
Associativity: in a sequence of three elements, remembering that we can really only combine two at a time, it does not matter whether the middle element is combined with the first element or the last element. The associative property is possessed by the natural numbers under addition, e.g. $(2 + 3) + 7 = 2 + (3 + 7)$.

Identity or **neutral** element: there is just one element which, when combined with any other element, does not change it (in the above example, this is the operation 'leave it as it is', or 'stay put').

Inverse element: each element has one element which 'undoes' the operation (for each operation there was **one** operation which produced the same result as the neutral operation on its own, i.e. which returned the square to its original starting position).

The above was included to outline some of the basic structure. It should not be presented to children in this way, but it is possible through discussion and reference to the tables and through actual movement of the square to introduce each property with children. For instance, they can find that combining two operations is the same as doing one on its own, that no new operation is necessary. This is an example of closure. Similarly the order of doing three operations can be investigated to illustrate the associative property. The one identity or neutral element can be found — it is easy to see which operation has no effect on the others. And the operations which return each operation to the starting position illustrate the inverse elements. The idea of group structure is thus quite straightforward for children to experience in a geometrical setting, and offers a good starting-point for further investigation with numbers as outlined in *Computation and Structure* ❸ .

Having looked at the rotations of a square in this way, teachers can discuss other shapes (rectangle, equilateral triangle, and possibly the regular hexagon) in a similar way and look for group structure in each case.

There is one other property we might look at. This is the commutative property (see *Computation and Structure* ❷).
There we saw that for addition of the natural numbers $3+7=7+3$, the order in addition can be interchanged.

Already children will have discovered from their actual operations on the square and from study of the tables, that the order of combining operations can be interchanged, e.g. R₂

followed by R₃ gives the same result as R₃ followed by R₂, and so on.

If a group of elements possesses this property in addition to the other four, it is said to be a **commutative** or **Abelian** group (after the Norwegian mathematician N. H. Abel who lived in the early part of the 19th century).